THIRD GRADE MAT[H]

Table of Contents

MW00380256

Introduction

Mathematics skills are utilized in every aspect of an individual's life, whether a student or an adult. These skills, however, involve more than just the computation of numbers. Organization, investigation, logical reasoning, and communication are also basic skills associated with mathematics. Students must develop a solid foundation in basic mathematics skills in order to meet the challenges of learning. Once armed with these tools, they can face new situations with confidence in their ability to solve problems and to make decisions.

The *Third Grade Math* program is offered to develop and strengthen mathematics skills. Each page provides practice in one specified skill. The worksheet can be used to assess students' understanding of the concept before or after the classroom lesson, or it can be used by students who might benefit from additional practice, either at home or school.

Organization

Eleven units cover the basic mathematics skills taught in the third grade. Students begin with a review of addition and subtraction facts and place value. They move on to practice skills dealing with time and money. Students then proceed to learning multiplication and division facts. Finally, the book focuses on geometry, measurement, fractions, and decimals. Fun, thematic worksheet titles attract students' interest. One page at the end of each unit is devoted solely to word problems which show how the learned skill might be applied to a real-world situation. These problems also provide practice in using a variety of problem-solving strategies.

Special Features

Each worksheet serves as practice for only one basic mathematics skill. Students who may need additional practice could benefit from these pages. Each page in the *Third Grade Math* book also ends with a word problem. These problems deal only with the skill students are practicing. These word problems also provide examples of how mathematics skills can be applied to the real world.

Use

This book is designed for independent use by students who have had instruction in the specific skills covered in the lessons. Copies of the worksheets can be given to individuals, pairs of students, or small groups for completion. The worksheets can also be given as homework for reviewing and reinforcing basic mathematics skills.

To begin, determine the implementation that fits your students' needs and your classroom structure. The following plan suggests a format for this implementation:

1. Explain the purpose of the worksheets to your class.
2. Review the mechanics of how you want students to work with the exercises.
3. Review the specific skill for the students who may not remember the process for successful completion of the computation.
4. Introduce students to the process and to the purpose of the activities.
5. Do a practice activity together.
6. Discuss how students can use the skill as they work and play.

Additional Notes

1. A letter to parents is included on page 4. Send it home with the students and encourage them to share it with their parents.
2. Have fun with the pages. Math should be an enjoyable adventure that helps students grow, not only in math, but in their confidence and their ability to face new and challenging experiences.

Dear Parent,

Mathematics skills are important tools that your child will use throughout his or her life. These skills encompass more than just the computation of numbers. They involve the ability of individuals to organize, investigate, reason, and communicate. Thus, your child must develop a strong foundation of basic mathematics skills in the elementary grades so that he or she can expand and build on these skills to help navigate through the life experiences.

During the year, your child will be learning and practicing many mathematics skills in class. Some of the skills include adding and subtracting two and three-digit numbers, multiplying, dividing, telling time to the minute, and working with standard and metric units of measurement. After exploring the concepts associated with these basic skills, your child will bring home worksheets, whether completed in class or to be completed at home, designed to further practice these skills. To help your child progress at a faster rate, please consider the following suggestions:

- Together, review the work your child brings home or completes at home. Discuss any errors and encourage your child to correct them.
- Encourage your child to make up word problems which apply to newly learned skills.
- Guide your child to see why it is important to learn math by pointing out ways that math is used in everyday life.
- Play games and solve puzzles with your child that utilize math skills.

Thank you for your help. Your child and I appreciate your assistance and reinforcement in this learning process.

Cordially,

Name _____   Date _____

• • • • • • • • • WATCH FOR THE SIGNS • • • • • • • • •

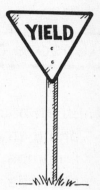

 Solve.

1. $9 + 1 = $ ___   **2.** $16 - 8 = $ ___   **3.** $7 + 5 = $ ___

4. $4 \times 7 = $ ___   **5.** $6 \times 6 = $ ___   **6.** $13 - 4 = $ ___

7. $35 \div 5 = $ ___   **8.** $64 \div 8 = $ ___   **9.** $24 \times 2 = $ ___   **10.** $49 - 21 = $ ___

11. $30 \times 3 = $ ___   **12.** $500 + 100 = $ ___   **13.** $33 \div 8 = $ ___   **14.** $400 \times 2 = $ ___

15. $\begin{array}{r} 6 \\ \times\ 3 \\ \hline \end{array}$ **16.** $\begin{array}{r} 7 \\ -\ 4 \\ \hline \end{array}$ **17.** $9\overline{)9}$ **18.** $\begin{array}{r} 8 \\ +\ 5 \\ \hline \end{array}$ **19.** $\begin{array}{r} 2 \\ \times\ 0 \\ \hline \end{array}$

20. $\begin{array}{r} 4 \\ \times\ 5 \\ \hline \end{array}$ **21.** $2\overline{)62}$ **22.** $\begin{array}{r} 41 \\ \times\ 2 \\ \hline \end{array}$ **23.** $\begin{array}{r} 79 \\ +\ 8 \\ \hline \end{array}$ **24.** $3\overline{)47}$

25. $\begin{array}{r} 62 \\ \times\ 5 \\ \hline \end{array}$ **26.** $\begin{array}{r} 28 \\ +\ 47 \\ \hline \end{array}$ **27.** $\begin{array}{r} 50 \\ -\ 34 \\ \hline \end{array}$ **28.** $\begin{array}{r} 413 \\ -\ 95 \\ \hline \end{array}$ **29.** $\begin{array}{r} 603 \\ -\ 468 \\ \hline \end{array}$

   **30.** $\begin{array}{r} \$5.90 \\ +\ 1.79 \\ \hline \end{array}$ **31.** $\begin{array}{r} 828 \\ +\ 861 \\ \hline \end{array}$ **32.** $\begin{array}{r} 942 \\ -\ 375 \\ \hline \end{array}$

····· BRUSH UP ON PROBLEM SOLVING ·····

 Choose the strategy and solve.

1. Ethan has 7 large paint brushes and 8 small paint brushes. Write a number sentence to tell how many paint brushes Ethan has.

_____

2. About 378 people visited the art museum on Monday. To the nearest hundred, about how many people visited the art museum that day?

_____

3. Stan buys paints for $2.95. How much change will he get back from $5.00?

_____

4. Nathan began painting at 2:30. He painted for 1 hour. At what time did Nathan stop painting?

_____

5. Kung paid for a box of crayons using 3 quarters, 1 dime, and 4 pennies. How much money did the crayons cost?

_____

6. Some crayons are divided equally among 3 students. Each student gets 8 crayons. How many crayons are there?

_____

7. Jeremiah paints on a sheet of paper that measures 2 feet long and 6 feet wide. What is the perimeter of the paper?

_____

8. Yoko combines 875 mL of white paint and 250 mL of red paint. Does Yoko make *more* than or *less* than 1,000 mL of pink paint?

_____

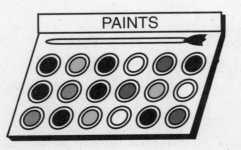

PAINTS

• • • • • • • • • • • • • • • • • HOP TO IT! • • • • • • • • • • • • • • • •

 Complete the addition sentence.

1. 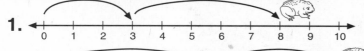 $3 + 5 =$ ___

2. $6 + 4 =$ ___

3. $2 + 6 =$ ___

4. $4 + 5 =$ ___

Find the sum.

5. 3 + 5	**6.** 7 + 4	**7.** 6 + 5	**8.** 8 + 4	**9.** 9 + 6
10. 7 + 7	**11.** 6 + 7	**12.** 9 + 2	**13.** 9 + 3	**14.** 8 + 2

15. $3 + 6 =$ ___   **16.** $2 + 9 =$ ___   **17.** $8 + 8 =$ ___

18. $5 + 5 =$ ___   **19.** $8 + 7 =$ ___   **20.** $4 + 6 =$ ___

Real World Connection

Write the number sentence and solve.

21. Meg sees 4 frogs sitting on a log. She sees 2 more frogs hop on the log. How many frogs are sitting on the log now?

_____

Name _____   Date _____

• • • • • • • • • • • • DOUBLE THE FUN • • • • • • • • • • • •

 Find the sum.

1. 6
   + 6

2. 4
   + 5

3. 3   4. 7   5. 6   6. 8   7. 9   8. 2
   + 3   + 8   + 9   + 5   + 8   + 3

9. 5   10. 6   11. 3   12. 2   13. 8   14. 4
   +5   + 7   + 8   + 2   + 7   + 7

15. 5 + 8 = ____   16. 6 + 5 = ____   17. 4 + 4 = ____

18. 8 + 9 = ____   19. 5 + 9 = ____   20. 7 + 7 = ____

21. 9 + 7 = ____   22. 7 + 6 = ____   23. 9 + 9 = ____

24. 8 + 8 = ____   25. 4 + 5 = ____   26. 8 + 6 = ____

27. 5 + 5 = ____   28. 6 + 6 = ____   29. 7 + 8 = ____

Real World Connection

Write the number sentence and solve.

30. Linda and Marie collect stamps. Linda has 8 stamps. Marie has one more than Linda. How many stamps do the girls have together?

_____

Name _____   Date _____

· · · · · · · · · · · · PENGUIN PLAY · · · · · · · · · · · · · ·

 Find the sum.

 +

1. 9 + 6 = ___

2. 6 + 9 = ___

3. 4 + 0 = ___

4. 0 + 4 = ___

5. 5 + 0 = ___   **6.** 0 + 6 = ___   **7.** 2 + 0 = ___

8. 0 + 8 = ___   **9.** 9 + 0 = ___   **10.** 0 + 7 = ___

11.   5   7   **12.**   6   8   **13.**   3   9
        +7   +5   +8   +6   +9   +3

 Use order in addition to write another addition fact.

14. 8 + 7= 15, so ___ + ___ = ___   **15.** 9 + 4 = 13, so ___ + ___ = ___

Real World Connection

Write the number sentence and solve.

16. Lillian threw fish to two penguins. All the fish were caught. One penguin caught 7 fish. The other penguin caught no fish. How many fish did Lillian throw?

_____

www.svschoolsupply.com   Number Facts: Order and Zero

© Steck-Vaughn Company   9   Math 3, SV 8047-2

Name _____   Date _____

•••••••••• DOG-GONE ADDITION ••••••••••

Look for tens. Find the sum.

1. 6 + 4 + 3 = ___   Did you find a ten? ___

2. 5 + 5 + 2 = ___   **3.** 4 + 2 + 8 = ___   **4.** 6 + 1 + 5 = ___

5. 3 + 7 + 8 = ___   **6.** 2 + 4 + 6 = ___   **7.** 9 + 1 + 1 = ___

8. 3 + 2 + 8 = ___   **9.** 7 + 2 + 2 = ___   **10.** 5 + 5 + 5 = ___

11.	**12.**	**13.**	**14.**	**15.**	**16.**
8	4	7	6	9	3
1	6	5	4	0	3
+ 9	+ 3	+ 5	+ 7	+ 4	+ 7

17.	**18.**	**19.**	**20.**	**21.**	**22.**
9	8	2	1	7	6
1	6	8	4	3	5
+ 7	+ 4	+ 5	+ 6	+ 8	+ 4

Real World Connection

Write the number sentence and solve.

23. Mrs. Goody has a pet store. There are 6 cocker
spaniels, 4 poodles, and 3 beagles at her store.
How many dogs does Mrs. Goody have?

_____

Number Facts: Grouping Addends
© Steck-Vaughn Company
Math 3, SV 8047-2

Name _____   Date _____

•••••••••••••••• JUMP BACK ••••••••••••••••

 Complete the subtraction sentence.

1. `0 1 2 3 4 5 6 7 8 9 10` $10 - 4 =$ ___

2. `0 1 2 3 4 5 6 7 8 9 10` $8 - 6 =$ ___

3. `0 1 2 3 4 5 6 7 8 9 10` $9 - 5 =$ ___

 Find the difference.

4. $\begin{array}{r} 8 \\ -5 \\ \hline \end{array}$ **5.** $\begin{array}{r} 7 \\ -3 \\ \hline \end{array}$ **6.** $\begin{array}{r} 6 \\ -2 \\ \hline \end{array}$ **7.** $\begin{array}{r} 10 \\ -3 \\ \hline \end{array}$ **8.** $\begin{array}{r} 9 \\ -7 \\ \hline \end{array}$

9. $\begin{array}{r} 7 \\ -4 \\ \hline \end{array}$ **10.** $\begin{array}{r} 6 \\ -3 \\ \hline \end{array}$ **11.** $\begin{array}{r} 9 \\ -6 \\ \hline \end{array}$ **12.** $\begin{array}{r} 9 \\ -4 \\ \hline \end{array}$ **13.** $\begin{array}{r} 8 \\ -7 \\ \hline \end{array}$

14. $7 - 5 =$ ___   **15.** $10 - 8 =$ ___   **16.** $8 - 1 =$ ___

17. $9 - 4 =$ ___   **18.** $6 - 4 =$ ___   **19.** $10 - 9 =$ ___

Real World Connection

Write the number sentence and solve.

20. Mr. Clark sees 8 grasshoppers in his garden. He catches 5 grasshoppers and puts them outside the garden. How many grasshoppers are left in Mr. Clark's garden?

_____

Name _____ Date _____

Find the difference.

1. 8
   − 8

2. 12
   − 3

3. 5
   − 5

4. 10
   − 0

5. 10
   − 5

6. 6
   − 0

7. 9
   − 0

8. 13
   − 4

9. 9
   − 9

10. 7
    − 7

11. 6
    − 6

12. 5
    − 0

13. 14 − 9 = ___

14. 8 − 0 = ___

15. 4 − 4 = ___

16. 5 − 0 = ___

17. 3 − 3 = ___

18. 7 − 0 = ___

Real World Connection

Write the number sentence and solve.

19. Jason is 7 years old on his birthday. He blows out all the candles on his cake. How many candles stay lit?

_____

• • • • • • • • • • • • • • • FAMILY FACT • • • • • • • • • • • • • • •

 Write the set of numbers for each fact family.

1. 4 + 8 = 12

8 + 4 =12

12 − 4 = 8

12 − 8 = 4

____ , ____ , ____

2. 6 + 7 = 13

7 + 6 = 13

13 − 7 = 6

13 − 6 = 7

____ , ____ , ____

Write the fact family for each set of numbers.

3. 7, 8, 15

___ + ___ = ___

___ + ___ = ___

___ − ___ = ___

___ − ___ = ___

4. 9, 4, 13

___ + ___ = ___

___ + ___ = ___

___ − ___ = ___

___ − ___ = ___

5. 6, 8, 14

___ + ___ = ___

___ + ___ = ___

___ − ___ = ___

___ − ___ = ___

 Find the missing number to complete each fact.

6. 9 + ___ = 15   6 + ___ = 15   15 − ___ = 9   15 − ___ = 6

Real World Connection

Write the number sentence and solve.

7. Including parents, Ethan has 3 girls and 4 boys in his family. Write a number sentence to tell how many people are in Ethan's family.

_____

Write the three other facts in the same fact family.

_____ , _____ , _____

Name _____ Date _____

•••••••••• TRACKING THE FACTS ••••••••••

Find the missing addend.

1. 5 + ___ = 12   **2.** 12 − ___ = 3   **3.** ___ + 7 = 13

4. 16 − ___ = 8   **5.** 15 − ___ = 6   **6.** 8 + ___ = 17

7. ___ + 9 = 13   **8.** ___ + 7 = 12   **9.** 5 + ___ = 14

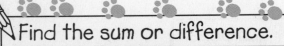
Find the sum or difference.

10.	**11.**	**12.**	**13.**	**14.**
8 + 5	5 + 9	13 − 7	16 − 8	9 − 9

15.	**16.**	**17.**	**18.**	**19.**
9 + 9	15 − 7	12 − 4	14 − 6	6 + 0

Complete each number sentence. Write + or − in the ◯.

20. 5 ◯ 9 = 14   **21.** 8 ◯ 3 = 5   **22.** 15 ◯ 6 = 9

23. 12 ◯ 7 = 5   **24.** 7 ◯ 4 = 11   **25.** 3 ◯ 8 = 11

26. 13 ◯ 6 = 7   **27.** 9 ◯ 8 = 1   **28.** 14 ◯ 7 = 7

Real World Connection

Write the number sentence and solve.

29. The Carlos family walked in the woods. Juan found 7 different
animal tracks. Juan's dad found 5 different tracks. How many
animal tracks did Juan and his dad find altogether? _____

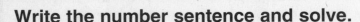

• • • • • • PROBLEM SOLVING WITH PETS • • • • • •

Strategies	• Act it Out • Guess and Check • Make a Model
	• Draw a Picture • Write a Number Sentence

Choose a strategy and solve.

1. Elaine and Juanita have 14 gerbils. Elaine has 2 more gerbils than Juanita. How many gerbils does each girl have?

_____

2. Ed walks his dog 15 minutes every day. He walks 3 minutes less at noon than after dinner. For how many minutes does Ed walk his dog each time?

_____

3. Hank spent $16 at the book sale. He spent $2 less on the fish book than he spent on the bird magazine. How much did Hank spend on each item?

_____

4. Marta has a total of 17 goldfish in her tank. She has 5 more lionhead fish than fantail fish. How many of each kind of goldfish does Marta have?

_____

5. Pete has 15 animals on his farm. He has 5 cows and 3 goats. The rest of the animals are chickens. How many chickens does Pete have on his farm?

_____

Name _____ Date _____

•••••••••• INTO THE HUNDREDS ••••••••••

Write the number.

1.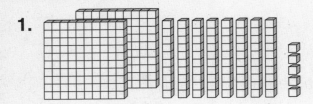

_____

2.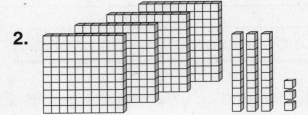

_____

3. 700 + 20 + 3 = _____

4. 100 + 0 + 9 = _____

5. 400 + 70 + 5 = _____

6. 300 + 10 + 6 = _____

7. five hundred seventy-nine _____

8. seven hundred forty _____

9. 4 hundreds 8 tens 5 ones _____

10. 6 hundreds 1 tens 0 ones _____

Real World Connection

Solve.

Pam is writing a news story for the school paper about the school cafeteria. The food service manager tells her that six hundred eighty-three slices of pizza and nine hundred forty-seven cartons of milk are served each day. What numbers should Pam write down?

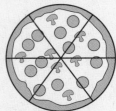

11. _____ slices of pizza

12. _____ cartons of milk

Name _____ Date _____

• • • • • • • • • • ARE WE THERE YET? • • • • • • • • • •

| Compare the numbers. Write < , > , or = in the ◯ . |

1.

Tens	Ones
2	3
3	1

23 ◯ 31

2.

Tens	Ones
5	0
4	9

50 ◯ 49

3.

Tens	Ones
8	5
8	5

85 ◯ 85

4.

Tens	Ones
7	9
9	0

79 ◯ 90

5.

Hundreds	Tens	Ones
2	8	0
2	0	8

280 ◯ 208

6.

Hundreds	Tens	Ones
4	8	5
4	8	4

485 ◯ 484

7. 7 ◯ 9   **8.** 47 ◯ 42   **9.** 85 ◯ 79   **10.** 91 ◯ 91

11. 467 ◯ 567   **12.** 2 ◯ 256   **13.** 921 ◯ 920   **14.** 860 ◯ 890

Real World Connection

Use the map to answer these questions.

15. Is Clarkville closer to Clear Valley or to Blue Mound?

_____

16. Is Blue Mound closer to Bruster or to Clarkville?

_____

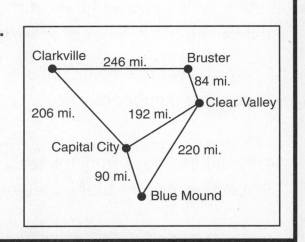

• • • • • • • • • • • • • LINE UP! • • • • • • • • • • • • • •

 Write the numbers in order from least to greatest.

1. 83, 87, 80   **2.** 38, 31, 35   **3.** 92, 96, 94

_____   _____   _____

4. 246, 251, 297   **5.** 897, 803, 830   **6.** 550, 505, 555

_____   _____   _____

 Write the numbers in order from greatest to least.

7. 337, 373, 341   **8.** 689, 698, 675   **9.** 762, 726, 750

_____   _____   _____

10. 501, 510, 515   **11.** 432, 423, 430   **12.** 907, 970, 957

_____   _____   _____

Real World Connection

Solve.

The Social Studies teacher at Westwood School took a survey to find out what field trip his students wanted to take. He made a table to show the most popular choices and the number of votes for each.

13. Which field trip idea got the greatest number of votes?

_____

14. Order the ideas from the least number of votes to the greatest.

_____

Students' Votes for Field Trips	
Field Trip Ideas	**Votes**
City Hall	55
Fire Station	87
Electric Company	23
Police Station	119

Name _____   Date _____

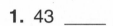

· · · · · · · · · GOING UP – GOING DOWN · · · · · · · ·

Round to the nearest ten cents or the nearest ten.

1. 43 _____   **2.** 79 _____   **3.** 89 _____

4. 61¢ _____   **5.** 33¢ _____   **6.** 47¢ _____

7. 62 _____   **8.** 85 _____   **9.** 54 _____

Write the numbers in each row that round to the number in the box.

10. 85 83 78 75 73 88 | 80 | _____

11. 63¢ 71¢ 65¢ 67¢ 69¢ | 70¢ | _____

Use the number line. Round each number to the nearest hundred.

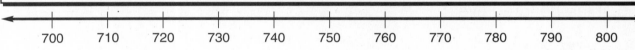

700   710   720   730   740   750   760   770   780   790   800

12. 785 _____   **13.** 742 _____   **14.** 719 _____   **15.** 752 _____

Round each number to the nearest hundred.

16. 587 _____   **17.** 279 _____   **18.** 848 _____   **19.** 920 _____

20. 328 _____   **21.** 489 _____   **22.** 176 _____   **23.** 512 _____

Real World Connection

Solve.

24. About 378 people visit City Park each week. To the nearest hundred, about how many people visit City Park each week?

_____

Name _____   Date _____

• • • • • • • • • • • • • • HOLD THAT PLACE • • • • • • • • • • • •

 Write the number.

1. 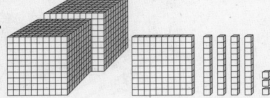   2.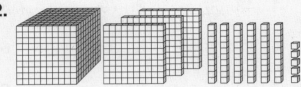

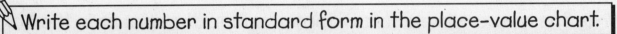

Write each number in standard form in the place-value chart.

Thousands	Hundreds	Tens	Ones

3. eighty-seven

4. four hundred thirty-two

5. nine hundred five

6. four thousand, seven hundred seven

7. six thousand, twenty-four

8. seven thousand, one hundred forty-five

9. two thousand, one

Real World Connection

Solve.

10. Mr. Huang needs to write a check for one thousand, four hundred twenty-seven dollars. How would the amount be written in standard form?

• • • • • • • • • • UNDER THE BIG TOP • • • • • • • • • •

 Write the number.

1. 30,000 + 8,000 + 400 + 70 + 1   **2.** 40,000 + 6,000 + 30 + 5

_____   _____

3. 50,000 + 4,000 + 700 + 20 + 3   **4.** 30,000 + 400 + 3

_____   _____

 Compare the numbers. Write < , > , or = in the ◯ .

5. 5,809 ◯ 4,908   **6.** 9,042 ◯ 8,998   **7.** 2,468 ◯ 1,357

8. 23,412 ◯ 19,246   **9.** 18,590 ◯ 18,650   **10.** 45,847 ◯ 45,847

Write the numbers in order from least to greatest.

11. 2,345	**12.** 32,076	**13.** 70,291	**14.** 99,909
22,486	32,570	68,921	99,900
12,123	23,676	69,129	99,099

_____   _____   _____   _____

_____   _____   _____   _____

_____   _____   _____   _____

Real World Connection

Solve.

15. Ms. Johnson recorded the number of toys sold in one month of the circus. Put the sales of balloons, stuffed lions, drinks, and clown hats in order from highest to lowest.

Toy		Number Sold
🎈	balloon	22,508
🦁	stuffed lion	11,897
🥤	drink	3,980
🎩	clown hat	7,256

······ NUMBERS OUT OF THIS WORLD ······

 Write the value of the digit 5 in each number.

1. 12,500 _____   **2.** 325,443 _____

3. 753,219 _____   **4.** 543,210 _____

 Write each number.

5. 200,000 + 30,000 + 2,000 + 70 + 4 _____

6. seventy thousand, eight hundred twenty _____

Complete the table. Use a calculator to find the numbers that are 1,000 more, 10,000 more, and 100,000 more.

	Number	1,000 More	10,000 More	100,000 More
7.	31,096			
8.	249,861			
9.	890,421			
10.	621,940			

Real World Connection

Solve.

11. From one side of Saturn's ring to the other, it is about one hundred sixty-nine thousand, three hundred miles. Write the miles in numbers.

_____

•••••••••• WHAT COMES NEXT? ••••••••••

 Tell whether each number is *odd* or *even*.

1. 62 _____   **2.** 29 _____   **3.** 417 _____

4. 140 _____   **5.** 1,243 _____   **6.** 27,456 _____

 Write the missing numbers in the pattern.

7. 10, _____, 30, 40, _____, _____, 70

8. 35, 30, _____, 20, _____, _____, 5

9. 23, 25, 27, _____, _____, 33, _____

10. 7, 14, 21, _____, _____, _____

11. 4, 12, 20, _____, _____, _____

12. 54, 48, 42, _____, _____, _____

Real World Connection

Solve.

13. Dan noticed a pattern at his school. The classroom doors are numbered with every other odd number. They begin at 21 and end at 49. Write the numbers.

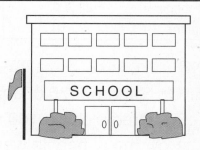

____ ____ ____ ____

____ ____ ____ ____

····· PROBLEM SOLVING ON THE ROAD ·····

Choose a strategy and solve.

1. Sonya drove 46 miles to the ballgame, and Vicki drove 51 miles. Who traveled farther?

_____

2. A bus traveled 557 miles south and 657 miles east. In which direction did it travel farther?

_____

3. Kathy's suitcase weighs between 20 and 30 pounds, but she thinks it weighs closer to 20 pounds. What could be the weight of her suitcase?

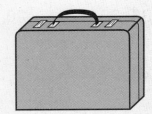

_____

Areas of the Great Lakes	
Name	Area (in square miles)
Huron	23,000
Superior	31,700
Erie	9,910
Michigan	22,300
Ontario	7,550

4. Roland visits the two largest Great Lakes. Using the table, order the areas of the lakes from greatest to least. Circle the two largest lakes to show which places Roland visits.

_____

5. On Sunday, 375,000 people visited state parks. By three o'clock, 100,000 people had gone home. How many people were still at the parks?

_____

•••••••••• TOY SHOP ESTIMATES ••••••••••

| Estimate each sum or difference by rounding. Show your work. |

1. 48 _____ **2.** 21 _____ **3.** 87 _____
      + 19 + _____   + 67 + _____   − 41 − _____

4. 89 _____ **5.** 70 _____ **6.** 62 _____
      + 53 + _____   − 27 − _____   + 98 + _____

7. 39 _____ **8.** 57 _____ **9.** 66 _____
      + 72 + _____   − 18 − _____   + 23 + _____

Real World Connection

Solve.

10. You are told that you can spend "about 50¢" to buy 2 items at the toy store. Which 2 items can you choose?

50¢

63¢

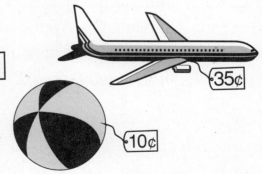
35¢

10¢

_____

Name _____ Date _____

•••••••••••••••••1, 2, 3 GO!•••••••••••••••••

Find the sum.

1. 78
   + 27

2. 55
   + 96

3. 9
   + 97

4. 88
   + 34

5. 81
   + 33

6. 67
   + 58

7. 91
   + 43

8. 41
   + 37

9. 43
   + 77

10. 32
    + 46

11. 48
    + 97

12. 32
    + 26

13. 39
    + 87

14. 87
    32
    + 19

15. 71
    39
    + 42

16. 22
    46
    + 38

17. 54
    19
    + 68

18. 65
    59
    + 11

Real World Connection

Write the number sentence and solve.

19. Gary likes to run in marathons. He runs several
    times each week to get in shape. On Monday,
    Gary runs 13 miles. On Wednesday, he runs 16
    miles. On Saturday, Gary runs 11 miles. How
    many miles in all does Gary run this week?

_____

Name _____   Date _____

• • • • • • • • • • • • STEPPING DOWN • • • • • • • • • • • •

| Find the difference.

1.　98
　 − 29

2.　51
　 − 18

3.　82
　 − 41

4.　72
　 − 28

5.　83
　 − 67

6.　75
　 − 54

7.　37
　 − 19

8.　93
　 − 56

9.　92
　 − 48

10.　71
　 − 48

11.　70
　 − 18

12.　88
　 − 78

13.　87
　 − 27

14.　48
　 − 39

15.　68
　 − 40

16.　34
　 − 29

Real World Connection

Write the number sentence and solve.

17. Bill lives on the 25th floor of an apartment
building. Bill's friend lives on the 19th floor.
How many floors does Bill pass when he goes
down to visit his friend?

_____

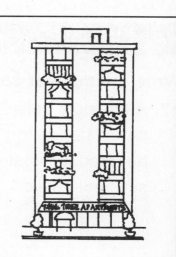

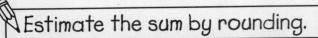

ROUND ABOUT

 Estimate the sum by rounding.

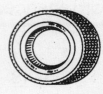

1. 388
   + 412

2. 479
   + 596

3. 218
   + 195

4. 165
   + 815

5. 321
   + 780

6. 275
   + 443

7. 867
   + 759

8. 963
   + 529

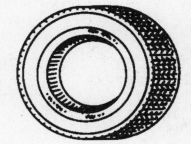

9. 648
   + 265

10. 479
    + 762

11. 219
    + 425

12. 617
    + 189

13. 476
    + 207

14. 246
    + 713

15. 369
    + 369

16. 427
    + 394

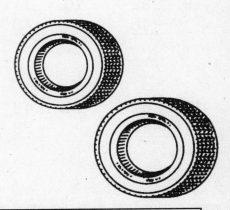

Real World Connection

Write the number sentence and solve.

17. A tire store sells 278 tires on Thursday. It sells 112 tires on Friday. To the nearest hundred, estimate how many tires the store sells both days.

_____

Name _____ Date _____

• • • • • • • • • • • • • *IT ALL ADDS UP!* • • • • • • • • • • • •

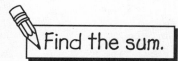
Find the sum.

1. 268
   + 409

2. 435
   + 943

3. 119
   + 605

4. 34
   + 128

5. 328
   + 851

6. 768
   + 126

7. 418
   + 475

8. 689
   + 410

9. 209
   + 68

10. 323
   + 524

11. 353
   + 139

12. 220
   + 719

13. 468
   123
   + 372

14. 203
   75
   + 849

15. 452
   268
   + 173

16. 511
   89
   + 265

Real World Connection

Write the number sentence and solve.

17. During a Math-A-Thon, Xing completes 284
math problems and 121 word problems. How
many problems does Xing complete in all?

_____

Name _____   Date _____

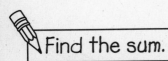

 Find the sum.

1. $3.14
   + 3.75

2. $5.98
   + 2.15

3. $4.15
   + 6.89

4. $9.08
   + .79

5. $6.18
   + 4.25

6. $5.72
   + 7.48

7. $3.61
   + 8.68

8. $7.59
   + 8.69

9. $8.93
   + 8.87

10. $7.47
    + 6.25

11. $5.63 + $8.96 = _____

12. $9.90 + $2.47 = _____

13. $4.82 + $2.99 = _____

14. $5.83 + $3.85 = _____

15. $3.50 + $1.74 = _____

16. $6.25 + $2.68 = _____

Real World Connection

Write the number sentence and solve.

17. Rita and Paul ride the bus to and from the museum. The fare each way is $2.20. How much do Rita and Paul each spend on bus fare?

_____

Addition and Subtraction: Adding Money

Math 3, SV 8047-2

•••••• PLAYING WITH SUBTRACTION ••••••

Find the difference.

1. 861
  – 644
	2. 853
	  – 427
		3. 590
		  – 46

4. 748
  – 145
	5. 870
	  – 543
		6. 965
		  – 247
			7. 785
			  – 183

8. 973
  – 48
	9. 697
	  – 160
		10. 375
		  – 125
			11. 892
			  – 537

12. 660
  – 435
	13. 897
	  – 369
		14. 768
		  – 265
			15. 723
			  – 119

Real World Connection

Write the number sentence and solve.

16. The theater sells 480 tickets in Week 1 and 612 tickets in Week 2. How many more tickets does the theater sell in Week 2?

_____

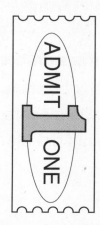

•••••• BOWLING IN THE HUNDREDS ••••••

 Find the difference.

1. 546
−459

2. 949
−368

3. 815
−438

4. 746
−209

5. 912
−798

6. 869
−679

7. 452
−317

8. 546
−281

9. 515
−495

10. 728
−384

11. 634
−509

12. 219 − 68 = _____

13. 489 − 392 = _____

14. 716 − 428 = _____

15. 563 − 277 = _____

Real World Connection

Write the number sentence and solve.

16. Hank bowls a score of 181 points and Marcie bowls a score of 214 points. How many more points did Marcie score than Hank?

_____

Name _____   Date _____

········ ZERO IN ON SUBTRACTION ········

| Find the difference. Choose **a**, **b**, or **c** to show how you regrouped. |

1.　503
　　　−258

a.
H	T	O
4	10	13

b.
H	T	O
4	9	13

c.
H	T	O
3	9	10

2.　800
　　　−349

a.
H	T	O
7	10	10

b.
H	T	O
7	9	10

c.
H	T	O
8	9	10

3.　602
　　　−498

a.
H	T	O
5	10	12

b.
H	T	O
6	9	12

c.
H	T	O
5	9	12

4.　960
　　　−386

a.
H	T	O
8	15	10

b.
H	T	O
8	15	0

c.
H	T	O
8	16	10

Find the difference.

5.　900
　　　−376

6.　807
　　　−295

7.　501
　　　−347

8.　203
　　　− 95

9.　904
　　　−369

Real World Connection

Write the number sentence and solve.

10. Beth and Joyce were in a rope jumping contest.
Beth jumped 200 times. Joyce jumped 115 times.
How many more times did Beth jump?

_____

Name _____   Date _____

·········· FISHING FOR ANSWERS ··········

Find the sum or difference.

1.   62
   − 15

2.   79
   + 2

3.   28
   + 47

4.   69
   + 21

5.   52
   − 29

6.   63
   − 28

7.   397
   + 215

8.   413
   − 295

9.   683
   + 106

10.   209
   − 84

11.   828
   + 861

12.   501
   − 347

13.   213
   + 95

14.   904
   − 369

15.   703
   + 287

16.   600
   − 401

17.   396
   + 197

18.   279
   + 83

19.   230
   − 229

20.   903
   + 468

21. $5.90
   − 1.79

Real World Connection

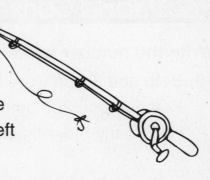

Write the number sentence and solve.

22. Noriko buys a spool of fishing line that has 300 yards in it. She uses 146 yards of the fishing line on her rod. How many yards of fishing line are left on the spool?

_____

Addition and Subtraction: Mixed Practice

Math 3, SV 8047-2

Name _____   Date _____

······· RACING TO SOLVE PROBLEMS ·······

Choose the strategy and solve.

1. Out of 36 people who sign up to race cars, only 27 actually race. How many people did not race?

_____

2. There are 321 people who buy tickets to watch the morning car races and 486 people who buy tickets to watch the afternoon car races. Estimate to the nearest hundred the total number of people who buy tickets to watch the car races that day.

_____

3. Tickets to the car races cost $15 for adults and $8 for children. How much will it cost for a family of two adults and one child to go to the car races?

_____

4. A sports car can go 192 kilometers per hour, but the top speed allowed on most U.S. highways is 88 kilometers per hour. How many more kilometers per hour can the car travel than it is allowed to?

_____

5. The total distance of a car race is 800 kilometers. If a car racer has traveled 489 kilometers, how many more kilometers must he drive to complete the race?

_____

Name _____   Date _____

• • • • • • • • • DAYS OF SUMMER • • • • • • • • • •

 Use the calendar for Exercises 1–8. Write the day of the week.

1. July 4   **2.** July 15

_____   _____

 Write the date one week before.

3. July 27   **4.** July 12

_____   _____

❀ ❀ ❀	JULY		❀	❀	❀	
S	M	T	W	T	F	S
				1	2	3
4	5	6	7	8	9	10
11	12	13	14	15	16	17
18	19	20	21	22	23	24
25	26	27	28	29	30	31

5. How many days are in July?   _____

6. How many Fridays are in July?   _____

7. What is the date of the second Wednesday?   _____

8. If July ends on a Saturday, on what day does
August begin?   _____

Real World Connection

Solve.

9. Jessica's birthday is on July 12. Today is
July 3. How many days are there until
Jessica's birthday?

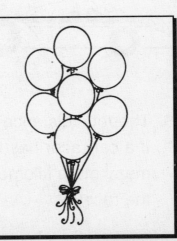

_____

Time: Calendar

Math 3, SV 8047-2

Name _____   Date _____

• • • • • • • • • • • • *IT'S ABOUT TIME* • • • • • • • • • • • •

 Circle the activity that will take longer.

1.

to eat dinner   or   to watch a movie

2.

to read a book   or   to brush your teeth

3.

to make a bed   or   to yawn

 Circle the better estimate.

4.   **5.**

to visit a museum   to bake a cake

3 minutes or 3 hours   4 minutes or 40 minutes

Real World Connection

Solve.

6. Joyce has about 45 minutes until her piano lesson.
She does her homework in 35 minutes. Circle the
activity Joyce can do before leaving to go to her lesson.

jump rope or play a ball game

TIME AFTER TIME • • • • • • • • • • • •

Write the time for each clock face.

1.   2.   3.

_____   _____   _____

 Begin at the 12. Write how many minutes the minute hand has moved. Count by fives. Use your clock face.

4.   5.   6.

_____   _____   _____

 Use your clockface.

A.   B.   C.

	Clock A	Clock B	Clock C
7. Write the time shown on each clock.	_____	_____	_____
8. Write the time 1 hour later than shown.	_____	_____	_____
9. Write the time 30 minutes later than shown.	_____	_____	_____

Real World Connection

Solve.

10. Fay asked her mother when the soccer game would start. Her mother told her that the minute hand would be on the 12 and the hour hand would be on the 3. What time would the soccer game start?

_____

Name _____ Date _____

•••••••••• MINUTE BY MINUTE ••••••••••

Count by fives to show the minutes that have passed from the first clock to the second clock.

1.

5, _____, _____, _____,
_____, _____

2.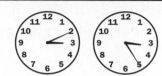

5, _____, _____

3.

5, _____, _____, _____,
_____, _____

4.

5, _____, _____, _____

Write the time 9 minutes later.

5.

6.

7.

_____   _____   _____

Real World Connection

Solve.

8. The children started jumping rope at 2:45. They jumped for 30 minutes. At what time did they stop jumping rope?

_____

Name _____   Date _____

GAME TIME PROBLEM SOLVING

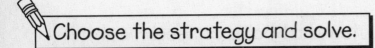

✏️ Choose the strategy and solve.

FEBRUARY						
S	M	T	W	T	F	S
	1	2	3	4	5	6
7	8	9	10	11	12	13
14	15	16	17	18	19	20
21	22	23	24	25	26	27
28						

1. Eric is playing in a basketball tournament February 20. What day will the tournament be?

_____

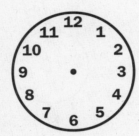

2. The basketball game ends when the hour hand is on the 4 and the minute hand is on the 8. Draw the hands on the clock. Write the time.

_____

3. Nathan's swim team practice began at 2:30. It lasted for 1 hour. At what time was the practice over?

_____

4. Deena played a game of tennis. Did it take about 2 minutes or about 2 hours?

_____

5. It took 2 hours and 15 minutes to play a football game. The game ended at 4:30. At what time did the game start?

_____

Math 3, SV 8047-2

•••••••••••••• **PIGGY BANKING** ••••••••••••••

 Write the amount.

1. 1 quarter   **2.** 2 quarters   **3.** 1 quarter
2 dimes   1 dime   3 nickels
3 pennies   4 nickels   8 pennies

_____   _____   _____

 Count the money and write the amount.

4.

_____

5.

_____

6.

_____

7.

_____

8.

_____

9.

_____

Real World Connection

Solve.

10.

Arch has these coins in his pocket. Circle the items he can buy.

75¢   49¢   63¢

Name _____ Date _____

··········· *THAT PRICE IS RIGHT* ···········

 Circle the letter of the matching amount.

1.    a.    b.    c.

2.    a.    b.    c.

Use play money to show two ways to make each amount. List the coins you use.

3.

_____

4.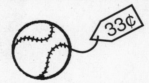

_____

Real World Connection

Solve.

5. Carmen has two $1 bills, 3 quarters, 3 dimes, and 4 pennies. Can she buy a book for $2.95?

_____

Math 3, SV 8047-2

•••••••••• *THE CHANGE IN STORE* ••••••••••

Use your play money. List the coins and bills you would receive in change.

Paid	Cost of Item	Change

1. 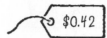 $0.42 _____

2. $1 bill $0.78 _____

3.  $2.47 _____

Use your play money. List the least number and type of coins you would receive in change from a $1 bill.

4. 58¢

_____

_____

5. 73¢

_____

_____

Real World Connection

Write the number sentence and solve.

6. Bart bought a gift for $7.79. He gave the clerk a $10 bill. How much change should he receive?

_____

• • • • PROBLEM SOLVING FOR A CHANGE • • • • •

Choose the strategy and solve.

1. Lani has 4 coins in her purse. They total 52¢. She has no dimes or nickels. What coins are in Lani's purse?

_____

2. Hans has three $1 bills, 3 quarters, and 2 pennies. Does he have enough money to buy the crayons?

_____

3. Gilda has four $1 bills, 2 quarters, 1 nickel, and 2 pennies. She buys the markers and the pencils. What coins does she have left?

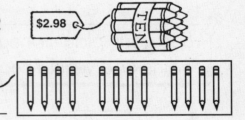

_____

4. Lucia bought a sandwich for 95¢. List two combinations of bills and coins she could use to pay for the sandwich.

_____

5. Don collects dimes. On Monday he added 7 dimes to his bank. Then he spent 5 dimes. Don has 12 dimes now. How many did he have to begin with?

_____

Name _____   Date _____

 Solve.

1. 3 ●●●
   +3 ●●●

2 threes = ___

2 × 3 = ___

2. 7 ■■■■■■■
   +7 ■■■■■■■

2 sevens = ___

2 × 7 = ___

3. 2 ♣♣
   2 ♣♣
   +2 ♣♣

3 twos = ___

3 × 2 = ___

 Write the addition sentence and the multiplication sentence for each picture.

4. ★ ★ ★ ★   ★ ★ ★ ★
   ★ ★ ★ ★   ★ ★ ★ ★

_____

_____

5. ▲▲▲ ▲▲▲ ▲▲▲
   ▲▲▲ ▲▲▲ ▲▲▲

_____

_____

 Draw a picture for each multiplication sentence.

6. 4 × 4 = 16   **7.** 3 × 3 = 9

Real World Connection

Solve.

8. Hannah arranges her stickers in 4 rows of 3. Write the addition and multiplication sentence to show how many stickers Hannah has.

_____

_____

Name _____   Date _____

• • • • • • • • • COME "2" THE GARDEN • • • • • • • • •

Complete the multiplication sentence for each picture.

1. ❀❀ ❀❀ ❀❀   2. ❀❀ ❀❀ ❀❀   3. ✳ ✳ ✳ ✳ ✳ ✳ ✳ ✳
   ❀❀ ❀❀   ❀❀ ❀❀ ❀❀   ✳ ✳ ✳ ✳ ✳ ✳ ✳ ✳

   5 × 2 = _____   6 × 2 = _____   2 × 8 = _____

Write the multiplication sentence for each picture.

4. ✤✤ ✤✤   5. ★ ★ ★ ★ ★ ★ ★   6. ❁ ❁ ❁
   ✤✤ ✤✤   ★ ★ ★ ★ ★ ★ ★   ❁ ❁ ❁

_____   _____   _____

Find the product. You may draw a picture.

7.   2   8.   9   9.   4   10.   7
   × 5   × 2   × 2   × 2

11.   2   12.   2   13.   2   14.   3
    × 8   × 6   × 2   × 2

Real World Connection

Write the number sentence and solve.

15. Sal has 6 rosebushes. He picks 2 roses from each
    bush. How many roses does he pick?

    _____

Multiplication: 2 as a Factor

Math 3, SV 8047-2

• • • • • • • • • • ON THE COUNT OF 3 • • • • • • • • • •

 Complete the multiplication sentence for each picture.

1. ☎☎☎☎☎☎☎☎
☎☎☎☎☎☎☎☎
☎☎☎☎☎☎☎☎

2. ☎☎☎☎
☎☎☎☎
☎☎☎☎

3. ☎☎ ☎☎ ☎☎
☎☎ ☎☎ ☎☎
☎☎ ☎☎ ☎☎

3 × 8 = _____

3 × 4 = _____

6 × 3 = _____

 Write the multiplication sentence for each picture.

4. ✈✈✈ ✈✈✈
✈✈✈ ✈✈✈

5. ✈✈✈✈✈✈✈
✈✈✈✈✈✈✈
✈✈✈✈✈✈✈

6. ✈✈✈✈✈✈✈✈✈
✈✈✈✈✈✈✈✈✈

_____   _____   _____

 Find the product. You may draw a picture.

7. 2
× 3

8. 9
× 3

9. 3
× 8

10. 7
× 3

11. 3
× 5

12. 3
× 6

13. 3
× 3

14. 4
× 3

Real World Connection

Write the number sentence and solve.

15. There are 5 shelves of footballs in a closet. Each shelf
has 3 footballs. How many footballs are there?

_____

Multiplication: 3 as a Factor

Name _____   Date _____

•••• PICTURE PERFECT MULTIPLICATION ••••

 Draw a picture for each multiplication sentence. Solve.

1. $8 \times 4 =$ _____

2. $4 \times 4 =$ _____

3. $7 \times 4 =$ _____

4. $4 \times 5 =$ _____

5. $5 \times 3 =$ _____

6. $6 \times 5 =$ _____

Find the product.

7. $\begin{array}{r} 8 \\ \times 5 \\ \hline \end{array}$

8. $\begin{array}{r} 4 \\ \times 6 \\ \hline \end{array}$

9. $\begin{array}{r} 7 \\ \times 5 \\ \hline \end{array}$

10. $\begin{array}{r} 5 \\ \times 5 \\ \hline \end{array}$

11. $\begin{array}{r} 4 \\ \times 9 \\ \hline \end{array}$

12. $\begin{array}{r} 5 \\ \times 9 \\ \hline \end{array}$

13. $\begin{array}{r} 4 \\ \times 3 \\ \hline \end{array}$

14. $\begin{array}{r} 2 \\ \times 5 \\ \hline \end{array}$

15. $3 \times 4 =$ _____

16. $4 \times 6 =$ _____

17. $4 \times 4 =$ _____

18. $4 \times 5 =$ _____

19. $5 \times 8 =$ _____

20. $6 \times 5 =$ _____

21. $7 \times 4 =$ _____

22. $5 \times 9 =$ _____

Real World Connection

Write the number sentence and solve.

23. Mabel colors 6 pictures with animals on them. Each picture has 4 animals. How many animals does Mabel draw?

_____

Multiplication: 4 and 5 as Factors

Math 3, SV 8047-2

Name _____ Date _____

•••••••••••• NOTHING TO DO! ••••••••••••

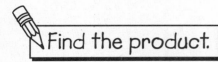 Find the product.

1. 9 × 0 = ___   **2.** 8 × 1 = ___

3. 7 × 1 = ___   **4.** 6 × 0 = ___

5. 4 × 0 = ___   **6.** 3 × 1 = ___

7. 9 × 1 = ___   **8.** 10 × 0 = ___   **9.** 8 × 0 = ___

10. 10 × 1 = ___   **11.** 7 × 0 = ___   **12.** 6 × 1 = ___

13. 4 ×0	**14.** 3 ×1	**15.** 2 ×0	**16.** 9 ×0	**17.** 1 ×1
18. 5 ×1	**19.** 3 ×0	**20.** 4 ×1	**21.** 2 ×0	**22.** 0 ×5
23. 1 ×2	**24.** 0 ×8	**25.** 1 ×8	**26.** 0 ×10	**27.** 6 ×1

Real World Connection

Write the number sentence and solve.

28. José wanted to start a stamp collection. He bought an 8-page stamp album. He could not find any stamps to put in the album. How many stamps did José put in his stamp album?

_____

Name _____   Date _____

······· THE ART OF MULTIPLICATION ·······

Write the multiplication sentence for each picture.

1. ✍ ✍ ✍
   ✍ ✍ ✍
   ✍ ✍ ✍

   _____

2. ✍ ✍ ✍ ✍ ✍
   ✍ ✍ ✍ ✍ ✍

   _____

3. ✍ ✍ ✍ ✍ ✍
   ✍ ✍ ✍ ✍ ✍
   ✍ ✍ ✍ ✍ ✍
   ✍ ✍ ✍ ✍ ✍

   _____

4. ✏✏✏✏✏✏✏✏✏
   ✏✏✏✏✏✏✏✏✏

   _____

5. ✏✏✏✏✏✏
   ✏✏✏✏✏✏
   ✏✏✏✏✏✏

   _____

6. ✏   ✏   ✏   ✏
   ✏   ✏   ✏   ✏
   ✏   ✏   ✏   ✏
   ✏   ✏   ✏   ✏

   _____

Find the product.

7. 4
   ×3

8. 3
   ×7

9. 5
   ×2

10. 7
   ×2

11. 8
   ×3

12. 4
   ×8

13. 5
   ×5

14. 3
   ×3

15. 6
   ×2

16. 2
   ×8

17. 2 × 6 = ___

18. 3 × 9 = ___

19. 4 × 5 = ___

20. 5 × 3 = ___

21. 5 × 6 = ___

22. 2 × 5 = ___

23. 3 × 4 = ___

24. 9 × 5 = ___

Real World Connection

Write the number sentence and solve.

25. The Craft Shop sells 5 boxes of crayons. There are 4 crayons in a box. How many crayons were sold?

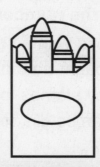

_____

Name _____   Date _____

• • • • • • • • • • • • • • LINE COUNTS • • • • • • • • • • • • • •

 Find the product.

1. 9 x 6 = ___

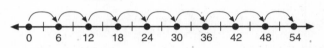

0 6 12 18 24 30 36 42 48 54

2. 8 x 7 = ___

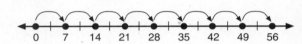

0 7 14 21 28 35 42 49 56

 Draw a number line to find the product.

3. 6 x 5 = ___   **4.** 7 x 6 = ___

5. 7 x 7 = ___   **6.** 6 x 8 = ___

Find the product.

7. 3 x 6	**8.** 4 x 6	**9.** 6 x 6	**10.** 6 x 8	**11.** 6 x 5

12. 7 x 3	**13.** 7 x 9	**14.** 5 x 7	**15.** 7 x 6	**16.** 2 x 7

Real World Connection

Write the number sentence and solve.

17. There are 8 students in each of 6 lines. How many students are in line?

_____

Multiplication: 6 and 7 as Factors

Math 3, SV 8047-2

Name _____ Date _____

 •••••••••••••• **IT'S A DOG'S LIFE** ••••••••••••••

Complete the table. Find the product.

1.

x	0	1	2	3	4	5	6	7	8	9
8										

2.

x	0	1	2	3	4	5	6	7	8	9
9										

 Find the product.

3. $9 \times 3 =$ ___   4. $4 \times 8 =$ ___   5. $8 \times 1 =$ ___   6. $2 \times 9 =$ ___

7. $8 \times 7 =$ ___   8. $9 \times 9 =$ ___   9. $8 \times 5 =$ ___   10. $9 \times 8 =$ ___

11.   3   12.   7   13.   9   14.   9   15.   9
   ×8   ×9   ×4   ×6   ×0

16.   4   17.   6   18.   6   19.   4   20.   9
   ×7   ×6   ×8   ×9   ×2

21.   1   22.   8   23.   7   24.   8   25.   9
   ×9   ×8   ×9   ×2   ×5

Real World Connection

Write the number sentence and solve.

26. A year in a human's life is said to equal 7 years in
    a dog's life. If a dog is 9 human-years old, what is
    its age in dog-years?

    _____

Multiplication: 8 and 9 as Factors

Name _____ Date _____

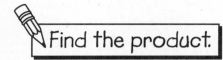
Find the product.

1. 3
×5

2. 5
×7

3. 8
×9

4. 7
×2

5. 2
×4

6. 9
×4

7. 8
×3

8. 6
×7

9. 2
×8

10. 6
×9

11. 8
×5

12. 7
×1

13. 9
×5

14. 8
×0

15. 5
×7

16. 9
×8

17. 6
×6

18. 7
×3

19. 5
×5

20. 4
×8

21. 4 × 1 = ___   **22.** 8 × 0 = ___   **23.** 1 × 9 = ___   **24.** 4 × 2 = ___

25. 0 × 6 = ___   **26.** 1 × 7 = ___   **27.** 3 × 2 = ___   **28.** 3 × 3 = ___

29. 5 × 2 = ___   **30.** 8 × 8 = ___   **31.** 0 × 9 = ___   **32.** 6 × 4 = ___

Real World Connection

Write the number sentence and solve.

33. Marty spends $3 per week to buy mystery books.
How much does he spend in 8 weeks to buy
mystery books?

Mystery!

_____

Name _____ Date _____

···PROBLEM SOLVING IS "SEW" MUCH FUN! ···

Choose the strategy and solve.

1. Hannah arranges some quilt squares in 4 rows of 3. How many quilt squares does Hannah have?

_____

2. Yarn is on sale for 5¢ a skein. How much will 9 skeins cost?

_____

3. Abby made a tapestry design out of 16 square fabric samples. The design is in the shape of a square. Make a model of the design. Draw your model in the space to the right.

_____

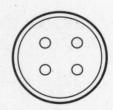

4. Thuy buys 7 cards of buttons. There are 8 buttons on each card. How many buttons does he have?

_____

5. Ellen buys 8 needles for $1.00. She spends $3.00. How many needles does she buy?

_____

Name _____   Date _____

SWEET DIVISION

Answer the question for each picture.

1. 🍁 🍁 🍁
   🍁 🍁 🍁

   How many in all? ___

   How many groups? ___

   How many in
   each group? ___

   6 ÷ 2 = ___

2. 🍁 🍁 🍁 🍁 🍁 🍁 🍁
   🍁 🍁 🍁 🍁 🍁 🍁 🍁
   🍁 🍁 🍁 🍁 🍁 🍁 🍁

   How many in all? ___

   How many groups? ___

   How many in
   each group? ___

   21 ÷ 3 = ___

3. 🍁 🍁 🍁 🍁
   🍁 🍁 🍁 🍁
   🍁 🍁 🍁 🍁

   How many in all? ___

   How many groups? ___

   How many in
   each group? ___

   12 ÷ 3 = ___

 Complete the division sentence for each picture.

4. ⚙ ⚙
   ⚙ ⚙

   4 ÷ 2 = ___

5. ⚙ ⚙ ⚙
   ⚙ ⚙ ⚙
   ⚙ ⚙ ⚙

   9 ÷ 3 = ___

6. ⚙ ⚙   ⚙ ⚙
   ⚙ ⚙   ⚙ ⚙
   ⚙ ⚙   ⚙ ⚙
   ⚙ ⚙   ⚙ ⚙

   16 ÷ 4 = ___

Real World Connection

7. A box holds 8 cookies.
   How many cookies will each person get?   8 ÷ 4 = ___

Name _____   Date _____

·········· PICTURE THESE FAMILIES ··········

 Use the pictures to solve.

1. ▲▲▲▲▲▲▲
   ▲▲▲▲▲▲▲
   ▲▲▲▲▲▲▲

   $3 \times 7 =$ ___
   $21 \div 7 =$ ___

2. ▲▲▲▲   ▲▲▲▲
   ▲▲▲▲   ▲▲▲▲
        ▲▲▲▲

   $5 \times 4 =$ ___
   $20 \div 4 =$ ___

 Write the set of numbers for each fact family.

3. $3 \times 2 = 6;$ $2 \times 3 = 6;$ $6 \div 3 = 2;$ $6 \div 2 = 3$ _____

4. $5 \times 7 = 35;$ $7 \times 5 = 35;$ $35 \div 5 = 7;$ $35 \div 7 = 5$ _____

 Write the fact family for each set of numbers.

5. 4, 6, 24   6. 2, 5, 10   7. 3, 9, 27

   _____   _____   _____

   _____   _____   _____

   _____   _____   _____

   _____   _____   _____

Real World Connection

Solve.

8. There are 18 students in Rosa's art class.
   They are working in groups of 3. Draw a
   picture to show how many groups there are.

Division: Fact Families

Math 3, SV 8047-2

Name _____   Date _____

• • • • • • • • • SAIL AWAY "2" DIVISION • • • • • • • • •

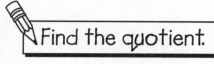

Find the quotient.

1. ⚓ ⚓ ⚓ ⚓ ⚓ ⚓
   ⚓ ⚓ ⚓ ⚓ ⚓ ⚓
   12 ÷ 2 = ___

2. ⚓ ⚓ ⚓ ⚓ ⚓
   ⚓ ⚓ ⚓ ⚓ ⚓
   10 ÷ 2 = ___

3. ⚓ ⚓ ⚓ ⚓
   ⚓ ⚓ ⚓ ⚓
   8 ÷ 2 = ___

4. ⚓ ⚓ ⚓ ⚓ ⚓ ⚓ ⚓
   ⚓ ⚓ ⚓ ⚓ ⚓ ⚓ ⚓
   14 ÷ 2 = ___

Find the quotient.

5. 8 ÷ 2 = ___   6. 4 ÷ 2 = ___   7. 12 ÷ 2 = ___

8. 16 ÷ 2 = ___   9. 18 ÷ 2 = ___   10. 10 ÷ 2 = ___

11. 6 ÷ 2 = ___   12. 14 ÷ 2 = ___   13. 16 ÷ 2 = ___

Real World Connection

Write the number sentence and solve.

14. Kim had 8 sheets of paper. He made 2 sets of paper boats. Each boat used 1 sheet of paper. How many boats were in each set?

_____

Name _____   Date _____

PLAYING WITH DIVISION

Write a division sentence for each.

1.

2.

_____   _____

Find the quotient.

3. $12 \div 3 =$ ___   **4.** $18 \div 3 =$ ___   **5.** $21 \div 3 =$ ___   **6.** $8 \div 2 =$ ___

7. $18 \div 2 =$ ___   **8.** $24 \div 3 =$ ___   **9.** $9 \div 3 =$ ___   **10.** $6 \div 3 =$ ___

11. $3\overline{)6}$ **12.** $2\overline{)12}$ **13.** $3\overline{)21}$ **14.** $3\overline{)27}$ **15.** $3\overline{)18}$

16. $3\overline{)3}$ **17.** $3\overline{)9}$ **18.** $3\overline{)15}$ **19.** $3\overline{)24}$ **20.** $3\overline{)12}$

Write **x** or $\div$ in the ◯.

21. $15 \bigcirc 3 = 5$ **22.** $4 \bigcirc 2 = 8$ **23.** $9 \bigcirc 3 = 3$ **24.** $3 \bigcirc 7 = 21$

25. $27 \bigcirc 3 = 9$ **26.** $12 \bigcirc 2 = 6$ **27.** $5 \bigcirc 2 = 10$ **28.** $3 \bigcirc 6 = 18$

Real World Connection

Write the number sentence and solve.

29. There are 15 chips in a game. If 3 children play, how many chips does each child get?

_____

Division: 3 as a Divisor

Math 3, SV 8047-2

Name _____ Date _____

FLYING HIGH WITH DIVISION

Write a division sentence for each.

1. ◆ ◆ ◆ ◆
   ◆ ◆ ◆ ◆
   ◆ ◆ ◆ ◆

2. ◆ ◆ ◆ ◆ ◆ ◆ ◆ ◆
   ◆ ◆ ◆ ◆ ◆ ◆ ◆ ◆
   ◆ ◆ ◆ ◆ ◆ ◆ ◆ ◆

_____  _____

Find the quotient.

3. $24 \div 4 =$ ___   4. $45 \div 5 =$ ___   5. $10 \div 5 =$ ___   6. $16 \div 4 =$ ___

7. $28 \div 4 =$ ___   8. $12 \div 4 =$ ___   9. $20 \div 4 =$ ___   10. $30 \div 5 =$ ___

11. $20 \div 5 =$ ___   12. $24 \div 4 =$ ___   13. $32 \div 4 =$ ___   14. $36 \div 4 =$ ___

15. $4\overline{)12}$ 16. $5\overline{)15}$ 17. $5\overline{)35}$ 18. $5\overline{)20}$ 19. $4\overline{)24}$

20. $5\overline{)25}$ 21. $4\overline{)20}$ 22. $4\overline{)28}$ 23. $5\overline{)45}$ 24. $4\overline{)32}$

25. $4\overline{)8}$ 26. $5\overline{)40}$ 27. $5\overline{)30}$ 28. $5\overline{)10}$ 29. $4\overline{)16}$

Real World Connection

Write the number sentence and solve.

30. A toy store orders a box of 35 kites. The box label says there are 5 kites of each color. How many colors of kites did the toy store order?

_____

Name _____   Date _____

MONKEY MAGIC

 Find the quotient.

1. 2 ÷ 2 = ___   **2.** 0 ÷ 2 = ___

3. 7 ÷ 1 = ___   **4.** 4 ÷ 4 = ___

5. 8 ÷ 1 = ___   **6.** 0 ÷ 5 = ___   **7.** 9 ÷ 9 = ___   **8.** 0 ÷ 4 = ___

9. 0 ÷ 6 = ___   **10.** 0 ÷ 1 = ___   **11.** 5 ÷ 1 = ___   **12.** 3 ÷ 3 = ___

13. 6 ÷ 1 = ___   **14.** 8 ÷ 8 = ___   **15.** 3 ÷ 1 = ___   **16.** 0 ÷ 7 = ___

17. 5$\overline{)5}$ **18.** 9$\overline{)0}$ **19.** 1$\overline{)4}$ **20.** 6$\overline{)6}$

21. 8$\overline{)0}$ **22.** 7$\overline{)7}$ **23.** 3$\overline{)0}$ **24.** 1$\overline{)9}$

Real World Connection

Write the number sentence and solve.

25. There were 8 balls in a magician's hat. The magician gave the same number of balls to 8 children. How many balls did each child get?

_____

Division: 0 and 1 as Divisors

© Steck-Vaughn Company

Math 3, SV 8047-2

·········· FIRED UP ABOUT DIVISION ········

Draw a picture for each division sentence. Solve.

1. 16 ÷ 4 = ___   **2.** 10 ÷ 5 = ___   **3.** 3 ÷ 3 = ___

Write two division sentences for each picture.

4. 🔥🔥🔥🔥🔥
🔥🔥🔥🔥🔥
🔥🔥🔥🔥🔥

5. 🔥🔥🔥🔥🔥🔥
🔥🔥🔥🔥🔥🔥

6. 🔥🔥🔥🔥

_____   _____   _____

_____   _____   _____

Find the quotient.

7. 18 ÷ 3 = ___   **8.** 24 ÷ 4 = ___   **9.** 25 ÷ 5 = ___   **10.** 0 ÷ 2 = ___

11. 15 ÷ 5 = ___   **12.** 14 ÷ 2 = ___   **13.** 12 ÷ 4 = ___   **14.** 20 ÷ 4 = ___

15. 4)‾28   **16.** 2)‾8   **17.** 3)‾24   **18.** 5)‾40   **19.** 1)‾8

20. 3)‾12   **21.** 5)‾5   **22.** 3)‾9   **23.** 4)‾36   **24.** 5)‾20

Real World Connection

Write the number sentence and solve.

25. Hillside Fire Station has 24 workers. They are grouped into teams of 3 fire fighters each. How many teams are at the Hillside Fire Station?

_____

Name _____ Date _____

KITTENS FOR SALE

Find the quotient.

1. $18 \div 6 =$ ___
2. $28 \div 7 =$ ___
3. $0 \div 7 =$ ___

4. $12 \div 6 =$ ___
5. $63 \div 7 =$ ___
6. $36 \div 6 =$ ___

7. $21 \div 7 =$ ___
8. $42 \div 6 =$ ___
9. $48 \div 6 =$ ___

10. $0 \div 6 =$ ___
11. $42 \div 7 =$ ___
12. $56 \div 7 =$ ___

13. $6\overline{)24}$
14. $6\overline{)6}$
15. $7\overline{)35}$
16. $7\overline{)14}$
17. $6\overline{)54}$

18. $1\overline{)7}$
19. $7\overline{)7}$
20. $7\overline{)35}$
21. $1\overline{)6}$
22. $6\overline{)48}$

23. $7\overline{)49}$
24. $6\overline{)36}$
25. $6\overline{)30}$
26. $4\overline{)28}$
27. $3\overline{)24}$

Real World Connection

Write the number sentence and solve.

28. Patti's Pet Store has 24 kittens. They are kept in 6 cages. How many kittens are in each cage?

_____

Name _____ Date _____

·········· BLOOMING DIVISION ··········

Find the quotient.

1. 54 ÷ 9 = ___   **2.** 64 ÷ 8 = ___   **3.** 81 ÷ 9 = ___

4. 56 ÷ 8 = ___   **5.** 18 ÷ 9 = ___   **6.** 72 ÷ 8 = ___

7. 48 ÷ 8 = ___   **8.** 36 ÷ 9 = ___   **9.** 40 ÷ 8 = ___

10. 7)‾42   **11.** 9)‾81   **12.** 7)‾63   **13.** 9)‾9

14. 6)‾48   **15.** 9)‾45   **16.** 9)‾0   **17.** 9)‾63

18. 9)‾36   **19.** 9)‾27   **20.** 9)‾72   **21.** 8)‾40

Find the missing divisor.

22. 32 ÷ ___ = 4   **23.** 9 ÷ ___ = 9   **24.** 48 ÷ ___ = 8

25. 81 ÷ ___ = 9   **26.** 63 ÷ ___ = 7   **27.** 54 ÷ ___ = 9

Real World Connection

Write the number sentence and solve.

28. A florist orders 81 flowers and 9 vases for a dinner. A worker puts the same number of flowers in each vase. How many flowers does the worker put in each vase?

_____

Name _____ Date _____

.... A PARADE OF DIVISION FACTS ....

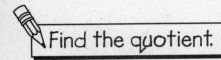

Find the quotient.

1. 27 ÷ 3 = ___   **2.** 54 ÷ 6 = ___   **3.** 7 ÷ 1 = ___

4. 5 ÷ 5 = ___   **5.** 40 ÷ 8 = ___   **6.** 63 ÷ 7 = ___

7. 36 ÷ 9 = ___   **8.** 12 ÷ 4 = ___   **9.** 0 ÷ 3 = ___

10. 7)‾49   **11.** 6)‾30   **12.** 5)‾20   **13.** 9)‾81

14. 2)‾0   **15.** 8)‾72   **16.** 3)‾18   **17.** 6)‾36

18. 4)‾4   **19.** 4)‾36   **20.** 8)‾64   **21.** 5)‾35

Real World Connection

Write the number sentence and solve.

22. There are 56 children who want to ride on floats in the parade. There are 8 floats. The same number of children will ride on each float. How many children will ride on a float?

_____

Name _____   Date _____

• • • • • • • • • • • • • • • LEFTOVERS • • • • • • • • • • • • • • •

 Find the quotient. Find how many are left.

1.

$2\overline{)5}$

What is the quotient?

_____

How many are left?

_____

2.

$5\overline{)12}$

What is the quotient?

_____

How many are left?

_____

 Find the quotient. Find how many are left.

3. $3\overline{)28}$ **4.** $4\overline{)32}$ **5.** $5\overline{)27}$ **6.** $8\overline{)35}$

7. $2\overline{)17}$ **8.** $9\overline{)83}$ **9.** $8\overline{)47}$ **10.** $6\overline{)37}$

11. $7\overline{)49}$ **12.** $4\overline{)39}$ **13.** $8\overline{)42}$ **14.** $4\overline{)19}$

15. $9\overline{)60}$ **16.** $7\overline{)58}$ **17.** $5\overline{)45}$ **18.** $7\overline{)25}$

Real World Connection

Write the number sentence and solve.

19. Mr. Sanchez bakes 25 muffins for a bake sale. He puts the muffins into packages of 4. How many muffins will Mr. Sanchez have left?

_____

Name _____   Date _____

• • • • • • • • • • EXTRA! EXTRA! • • • • • • • • • • • • •

| Find the quotient. Then check each answer by using multiplication. |

1. 86 ÷ 4   4)86

Check:

2. 47 ÷ 3   3)47

Check:

3. 35 ÷ 2   2)35

Check:

4. 53 ÷ 4   4)53

Check:

5. 55 ÷ 2   2)55

Check:

6. 58 ÷ 3   3)58

Check:

7. 69 ÷ 5   5)69

Check:

Real World Connection

Write the number sentence and solve.

8. Marco has 54 stamps in his stamp collection. Marco puts his stamps into groups of 4. How many groups of stamps does Marco have?

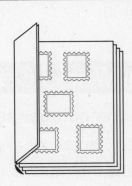

_____

Name _____ Date _____

• • • • • • • • • • • • • • NOT TIRED YET! • • • • • • • • • • • • • •

Write the number sentences to show the fact family for each picture.

1. ◎◎◎◎
   ◎◎◎
   ◎◎◎◎

2. ◎◎◎◎◎◎
   ◎◎◎◎◎

_____   _____

_____   _____

_____   _____

_____   _____

Find the product or quotient.

3. $6 \times 3 =$ ___   **4.** $14 \div 7 =$ ___   **5.** $36 \div 4 =$ ___   **6.** $8 \times 5 =$ ___

7. $56 \div 8 =$ ___   **8.** $81 \div 9 =$ ___   **9.** $9 \times 5 =$ ___   **10.** $0 \times 6 =$ ___

11. $1\overline{)9}$ **12.** $\begin{array}{r} 2 \\ \times\, 2 \\ \hline \end{array}$ **13.** $3\overline{)21}$ **14.** $\begin{array}{r} 7 \\ \times\, 8 \\ \hline \end{array}$ **15.** $9\overline{)36}$

16. $\begin{array}{r} 6 \\ \times\, 6 \\ \hline \end{array}$ **17.** $4\overline{)18}$ **18.** $\begin{array}{r} 8 \\ \times\, 9 \\ \hline \end{array}$ **19.** $3\overline{)44}$ **20.** $\begin{array}{r} 3 \\ \times\, 8 \\ \hline \end{array}$

Real World Connection

Write the number sentence and solve.

21. A tire company has 46 tires in stock. How many
cars can they service if each car gets 4 new tires?

_____

Name _____   Date _____

····· SOUNDS LIKE PROBLEM SOLVING ·····

Choose the strategy and solve.

1. A *duet* is a song played or sung by two musicians. Tell the number of duets a class could play if there are 18 students.

_____

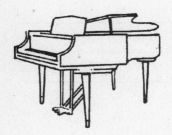

2. Greg practices piano for 20 minutes a day. He plays each piece he is assigned for 5 minutes. How many pieces does he practice each day?

_____

3. The third-grade class used rhythm instruments in their show. Twenty-four students shared 6 instruments. How many students shared each instrument?

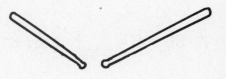

_____

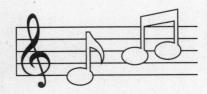

4. The class sang 8 songs. Each song lasted about 2 minutes. How many minutes did all of the songs take?

_____

5. Ms. Burns bought 6 tickets to a music concert. She gave the clerk $20. Ms. Burns got $2 back in change. How much did each ticket cost?

_____

Name _____ Date _____

• • • • • • • • • • • • • WINDOW COUNT • • • • • • • • • • • •

Write multiplication number sentences to describe the pictures.

1. ▯ ▯ ▯   2. 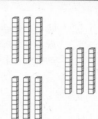   3.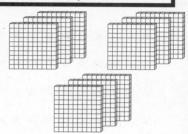

_____   _____   _____

Use mental math or place-value materials to complete.

4. 3 × 7 = 3 × 7 _____ = _____ ones = 21

    3 × 70 = 3 × 7 _____ = _____ tens = _____

    3 × 700 = 3 × 7 _____ = _____ hundreds = _____

5. 4 × 3 = ___   6. 3 × 9 = ___   7. 6 × 5 = ___

   4 × 30 = ___   3 × 90 = ___   6 × 50 = ___

   4 × 300 = ___   3 × 900 = ___   6 × 500 = ___

8.   50   9.   400   10.   30   11.   80   12.   900
   × 4   × 9   × 5   × 7   × 6

Real World Connection

Write the number sentence and solve.

13. The Clear View Company has to wash the windows of an 8-story apartment building. There are 60 windows on each floor. How many windows will the Clear View Company wash?

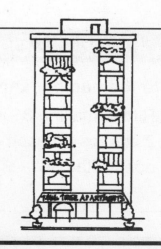

_____

2- and 3-Digit Multiplication: Tens and Hundreds

Math 3, SV 8047-2

Name _____   Date _____

• • • • • • • • • • IT'S IN THE MAIL • • • • • • • • • • • •

 Find the total.

1. ★★★★★★★★★★★★★★★
★★★★★★★★★★★★★★★
★★★★★★★★★★★★★★★
★★★★★★★★★★★★★★★

    4 groups of 15 = ____

    4 × 15 = ____

    15 × 4 = ____

2.

    3 groups of 24 = ____

    3 × 24 = ____

    24 × 3 = ____

Find the product. Draw a picture to help you.

3. 3 × 13 = ____   4. 5 × 15 = ____   5. 2 × 28 = ____

 Find the product.

6. 8 × 12 = ____   7. 4 × 16 = ____   8. 2 × 43 = ____

Real World Connection

Write the number sentence and solve.

9. Rita is mailing 31 invitations to her party. She puts
2 stamps on each envelope. How many stamps
does Rita use?

_____

Multiplication of Tens and Hundreds: Concept Development

Math 3, SV 8047-2

Name _____   Date _____

•••••••• STARRING – REGROUPING ••••••••

Find the product. Use place-value materials to help you.

1. 27
   × 2

2. 18
   × 3

3. 42
   × 2

4. 38
   × 2

5. 17
   × 5

6. 19
   × 4

7. 23
   × 4

8. 34
   × 2

9. 16
   × 5

10. 22
    × 4

11. 25
    × 3

12. 18
    × 2

13. 63
    × 2

14. 42
    × 3

15. 83
    × 2

16. 36
    × 4

17. 71
    × 5

18. 12
    × 8

19. 34
    × 5

20. 31
    × 6

21. 33
    × 4

22. 42
    × 4

Real World Connection

Write the number sentence and solve.

23. The students at Becker School are putting
    on a play. Each rehearsal lasts 2 hours. The
    students have 19 rehearsals. How many
    hours do the students rehearse for the play?

_____

Name _____   Date _____

•••••••• CAUTION! WILD DIVISION! ••••••••

Find the product.

1. 103
   × 8

2. 215
   × 3

3. 141
   × 7

4. 274
   × 2

5. 225
   × 4

6. 150
   × 5

7. 342
   × 5

8. 468
   × 2

9. 591
   × 4

10. 412
    × 8

11. 154
    × 6

12. 360
    × 3

13. 903
    × 5

14. 223
    × 4

15. 649
    × 2

16. 164
    × 5

17. 6 × 145 = ___

18. 7 × 24 = ___

19. 5 × 112 = ___

20. 4 × 106 = ___

21. 3 × 171 = ___

22. 8 × 93 = ___

Real World Connection

Write the number sentence and solve.

23. There are 112 acres in each section of a wildlife preserve. How many acres are in 7 sections?

_____

•••••••• CAN DO PROBLEM SOLVING ••••••••

Choose the strategy and solve.

1. Teri works at a recycling center. She earns $8 an hour. How much money does she earn in a 35-hour work week?

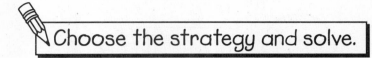

_____

2. Most states pay 5 cents per pound for recycled cans. Claire earned $50 by recycling cans. How many pounds of cans did Claire recycle?

_____

3. The students in each of 4 classes at Andian School recycled a total of 84 bags of cans in one year. Each class recycled an equal number of bags. How many bags did each class recycle?

_____

4. Students in 6 classes collected 5 bags of trash per class when they picked up trash along a road. Of all the trash collected, they were able to make 7 bags of cans. How many bags were not cans?

_____

5. The recycling center received 5,102 cans in March and 3,574 cans in April. How many more cans did the center receive in March than in April?

_____

Name _____   Date _____

• • • • • • • • • • • FIGURE IT OUT • • • • • • • • • • •

Cube

Cone

Cylinder

Sphere

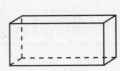
Rectangular Prism

Pyramid

Name the figure that each looks like.

1.

_____

2.

_____

3.

_____

4.

_____

5.

_____

6.

_____

7.

_____

8.

_____

9.

_____

Real World Connection

Solve.

10. Look around the room. Find 2 objects shaped like a cube. Write their names on the lines below.

_____

_____

Name _____   Date _____

 Name the figure that each looks like.

1.   _____

2. 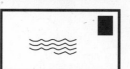 _____

3.   _____

4.   _____

5.   _____

6.   _____

✏ Draw a line from the description to the name of the figure.

7. 4 segments and 4 angles
All segments are the same length.   rectangle

                                                     circle

8. 4 segments and 4 angles
All segments are not the same length.   pentagon

9. 3 segments and 3 angles   square

10. 0 sides and 0 angles

11. 5 segments and 5 angles   triangle

Real World Connection

Solve.

12. Mr. Lewis is driving to the store. He stops
when he sees a stop sign. Draw a stop sign.
What shape is the stop sign?

_____

Geometry: Plane Figures

75   Math 3, SV 8047-2

Name _____   Date _____

 • • • • • • • • • • • • • • • • **TWINS** • • • • • • • • • • • • • • • •

> Tell whether the two figures are congruent. Write **yes** or **no**.

1.

2.

3.

4.

> Circle the figure that is congruent to the shaded figure.

5.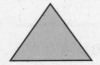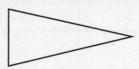

6.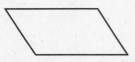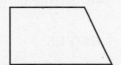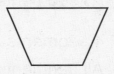

7.

Real World Connection

Solve.

8. Leisha and Meisha are making a quilt together.
   Leisha cuts a piece of fabric like the shape below.
   Meisha cuts a shape that is congruent to the one
   Leisha cuts. Draw the shape that Meisha cuts.

Name _____   Date _____

· · · · · · · · · · LOOK IN THE MIRROR · · · · · · · · · ·

 Trace the figure. Cut out your drawing and fold it in half.
Write **yes** or **no** to tell whether the figure has a line of symmetry.

1.
_____

2.
_____

3.
_____

4.
_____

 Is the dotted line a line of symmetry? Write **yes** or **no**.

5.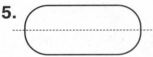
_____

6.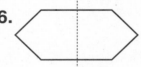
_____

7.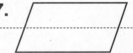
_____

8.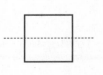
_____

9.
_____

10.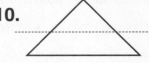
_____

Real World Connection

Solve.

11. In art, Mr. Ingles gave his students paper cut in
the shape to the right. He asked his students to
fold the paper along a line of symmetry. Draw a
line to show how the students can fold the paper.

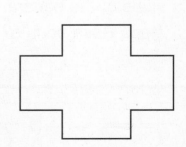

Geometry: Symmetry

77

Math 3, SV 8047-2

Name _____ Date _____

··········· GO ALL AROUND ···············

Cut out the paper clip ruler. Choose 3 books from your desk, classroom, or home. Find the perimeter of each book using the paper clip ruler. Then complete the table.

	Book	Guess	Perimeter
1.	Book 1		
2.	Book 2		
3.	Book 3		

Use the width of a crayon. Find the perimeter of each figure.

4. ___ units   5. ___ units

6. ___ units   7. ___ units

Real World Connection

Write the number sentence and solve.

8. The class wants to play Four Square. Rosa will make the lines of the game. She counts off 16 large steps for one side. She counts the same amount of steps for the other three sides of the square. What is the perimeter in steps Rosa counts?

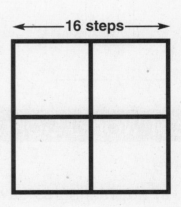

16 steps

_____

Name _____   Date _____

 ·············· **FAIR AND SQUARE** ··············

Find the area of each figure. Label your answer in square units.

1.

_____

2.

_____

3.

_____

4.

_____

5.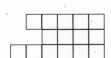

_____

6.

_____

 Fill in squares with your pencil. Make three shapes, each with an area of 6 square units.

7.

8.
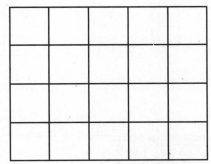

9.
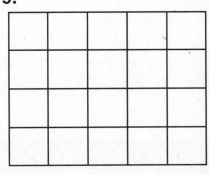

Real World Connection

Solve.

10. Mrs. Frazer bought a rectangle-shaped rug for her classroom. One side is 3 square units wide. Another side is 4 square units long. Fill in the squares to show how many square units the rug is.

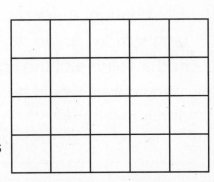

FISHY BUSINESS

 Find the volume of each shape.

1.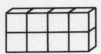

_____

2.

_____

3.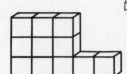

_____

4.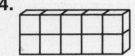

_____

5.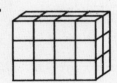

_____

6.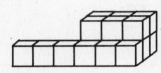

_____

7.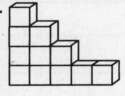

_____

8.

_____

9.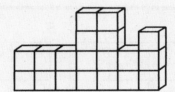

_____

Real World Connection

Write the number sentence and solve.

10. Allan bought a new aquarium. It was 2 times bigger than his old tank. He knew the old tank had a volume of the cubes to the right. How many cubes would he need to show the volume of his new tank?

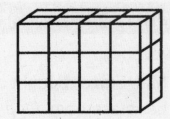

_____

Name _____   Date _____

••••• MAKE PROBLEM SOLVING A GAME •••••

 Choose the strategy and solve.

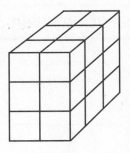

1. Alice needs to find a box that will hold all these blocks. What is the volume of the box?

_____

2. Sam measures the perimeter of a rectangle-shaped game field. The length of one side of the field is 42 long steps. The other side is 28 long steps. What is the perimeter of the field using long steps as the measure?

_____

3. Lana plays a game on the computer. Each shaded square unit shows the area Lana wins for answering a question correctly. How many square units does Lana win?

_____

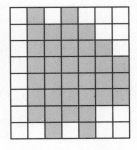

4. Chang buys a can of tennis balls. He sees that the can and the balls inside the can have different shapes. What solid figures do the balls and the can look like?

_____

5. Ernie cuts a heart out of paper. He folds the heart on the line of symmetry to make a card. Draw a line on the heart to show how Ernie folds the paper.

_____

Name _____ Date _____

• • • • • • • • • GOING THE DISTANCE • • • • • • • • • •

| Use your ruler. Measure the length of each in inches. |

1.   **2.**

_____   _____

3.

_____

| Draw each length from the • . |

4. 2 inches •   **5.** 1 inch •

6. 4 inches •

| Circle the better estimate. |

7.   **8.**

the length of a piece of paper   the distance from your home to school

11 inches or 11 feet   2 yards or 2 miles

9.   **10.**

the height of your chair   the distance a car travels

2 feet or 2 yards   20 yards or 20 miles

Real World Connection

Write the number sentence and solve.

11. Jorge connects 2-inch paper clips to make a chain.
How long is Jorge's chain if he uses 5 paper clips?

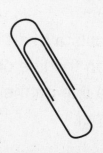

_____

········ NAME THAT MEASUREMENT ········

Which unit of measure would you use to weigh each item?
Write **ounce** or **pound**.

1. _____

2. _____

3. _____

4.  _____

 Tell which unit of measure you would use. Write **c, pt, qt** or **gal**.

5. milk in a glass
about 1 _____

6. water in an aquarium
about 10 _____

7. water in a cooler
about 4 _____

8. juice in a small carton
about 1 _____

Circle the better estimate.

9. 1 pound
or
1 ounce

10. 8 ounces
or
8 pounds

11. 1 quart
or
1 gallon

12. 1 pint
or
1 gallon

13. 5 pints
or
5 gallons

14. 1 cup
or
1 quart

Real World Connection

Solve.

15. A can with 3 tennis balls weighs 14 ounces. Do the
tennis balls weigh more than or less than 1 pound?

_____

Name _____   Date _____

• • • • • • • THE TEMPERATURE IS RISING • • • • • • •

Circle the more reasonable temperature.

1.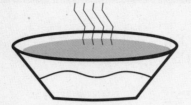

hot soup
50° F or 120° F

2.

sledding party
30° F or 80° F

3.

swimming party
15° F or 85° F

Write each temperature.

4.

5.

6.

7.

_____   _____   _____   _____

Real World Connection

Write the number sentence and solve.

8. When Eric woke up, the thermometer read 45° F.
Two hours later the temperature had risen 17°.
What was the temperature then?

_____

Name _____   Date _____

 **MAKE IT METRIC** ● ● ● ● ● ● ● ● ● ● ● ● ● ●

 Use your metric ruler. Measure the length of each in centimeters.

1. _____   **2.**

_____   _____

 Draw each length from the ●.

3. 2 centimeters ●   **4.** 3 centimeters ●

5. 12 centimeters ●

 Circle the better estimate.

6.   **7.**

the length of a chalkboard   the height of a child

8 centimeters or 8 meters   1 meter or 5 meters

8.      **9.**

the distance an airplane flies   the distance from the
                                     school office to your chair
70 meters or 700 kilometers
                                     30 meters or 300 kilometers

Real World Connection

Write the number sentence and solve.

10. Jared can hike 1 kilometer in about 9 minutes.
How long will it take him to hike 7 kilometers?

Name _____ Date _____

 ·· · · · · · · · FILLED TO CAPACITY · · · · · · · · · · ·

Which unit of measure would you use to weigh each item? Write *gram* or *kilogram*.

1.

an envelope

_____

2.

a crayon

_____

3.

a desk

_____

Choose the unit you would use to measure each. Write *milliliter* or *liter*.

4.

water in a thimble

_____

5.

milk in a cup

_____

6.

orange juice in a jug

_____

 Circle the better estimate.

7.

2 mL or 2 L

8.

250 mL or 250 L

9.

6 mL or 6 L

10.

10 g or 10 kg

11.

65 g or 65 kg

12.

25 g or 25 kg

Real World Connection

Write the number sentence and solve.

13. Ann filled her cat's 500-mL dish with milk. Now the dish has 175 mL of milk. How much did the cat drink?

_____

Name _____   Date _____

• • • • • • • • • • • • • • • HOT OR COLD • • • • • • • • • • • • • •

 Circle the more reasonable temperature.

1.

hot food

− 30°C or 70°C

2.

ice cube

20°C or 0°C

3.

picnic weather

20°C or 80°C

4.

room temperature

20°C or 70°C

5.

swimming weather

− 30°C or 30°C

6.

ice cream

20°C or − 5°C

 Write each temperature.

7.

8.

9.

_____   _____   _____

Real World Connection

Write the number sentence and solve.

10. Gretel bakes bread. Bread needs to bake at 150°C.
Gretel's oven does not work well. It cooks 20°C hotter than
it should. At what temperature should Gretel set her oven?

_____

•••••• GROW INTO PROBLEM SOLVING ••••••

Choose the strategy and solve.

1. Jeremiah buys tomato plants for his garden.
   He spaces them 18 inches apart. How
   many inches from the first plant is the
   third plant? Draw a picture.

_____

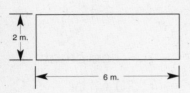

2. Jack's garden is a rectangle that measures 2
   meters long and 6 meters wide. What is the
   perimeter of the garden?

_____

3. Su-Lyn picks 2 pumpkins that weigh 12 pounds
   each. What is the total weight of the pumpkins?

_____

4. Edgar is recording the temperature in his garden
   for a science project. At 1:00 P.M., the temperature
   is 72° F. If the temperature rises 3 degrees every
   hour, what will the temperature be at 5:00 P.M.?

_____

5. Jane made a 25-L pot of soup using vegetables
   from her garden. She divided it equally into 5
   smaller containers for storage. How much
   vegetable soup does each container hold?

_____

·········· LOOKING FOR THE SHADE ··········

 Write the fraction for the part that is shaded.

1.   ☐ shaded parts
   ☐ parts in all

2.   ☐ shaded parts
   ☐ parts in all

3.

4.

5.

 Write the fraction for the part that is shaded.

6.

7.

8.

 Write the fraction for each word name.

9. one third   10. two fifths   11. four sixths

Real World Connection

Solve.

12. Sun-Yu shares one fourth of her sandwich with a friend. Shade the part of the sandwich Sun-Yu shares.

Name _____   Date _____

• • • • • • • • • • • • • • • • EQUAL PARTS • • • • • • • • • • • • • • •

✏️ **Write _true_ or _false_.**

1. $\frac{1}{3} = \frac{2}{6}$

_____

2. $\frac{1}{2} = \frac{1}{3}$

_____

3. $\frac{1}{2} = \frac{2}{4}$

_____

4. $\frac{3}{5} = \frac{1}{2}$

_____

5. $\frac{2}{3} = \frac{4}{6}$

_____

6. $\frac{5}{8} = \frac{2}{4}$

_____

✏️ **Name the equivalent fraction.**

7. $\frac{2}{4} = \frac{\square}{8}$

8. $\frac{5}{10} = \frac{\square}{2}$

9. $\frac{2}{5} = \frac{\square}{10}$

10. $\frac{4}{6} = \frac{\square}{3}$

11. $\frac{2}{8} = \frac{\square}{4}$

12. $\frac{6}{8} = \frac{\square}{4}$

Real World Connection

Solve.

13. Elaine and Joe each bought small pizzas for lunch. Elaine ate $\frac{1}{2}$ of her pizza. Joe ate the same amount of his pizza. Shade the amount of pizza Joe ate. Name the equivalent fraction.

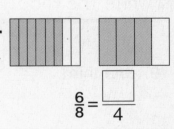

$$\frac{1}{2} = \frac{\square}{4}$$

Fractions and Decimals: Equal Fractions

Math 3, SV 8047-2

Name _____   Date _____

• • • • • • • • • • • • • WHO GETS MORE? • • • • • • • • • • • • •

 Compare. Write **<** or **>** in each ◯ .

 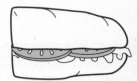

1.

$\frac{1}{3}$ ◯ $\frac{2}{3}$

2.

$\frac{3}{4}$ ◯ $\frac{2}{4}$

3.

$\frac{5}{6}$ ◯ $\frac{2}{3}$

 Compare. Write **<, >,** or **=** in each ◯ .

4.

$\frac{3}{5}$ ◯ $\frac{4}{5}$

5.

$\frac{2}{3}$ ◯ $\frac{4}{6}$

6.

$\frac{3}{4}$ ◯ $\frac{1}{2}$

7.

$\frac{4}{8}$ ◯ $\frac{1}{2}$

8.

$\frac{3}{5}$ ◯ $\frac{3}{8}$

9.

$\frac{2}{5}$ ◯ $\frac{4}{5}$

Real World Connection

Solve.

10. A bowl of muffin batter contains $\frac{1}{3}$-cup of oil and $\frac{2}{3}$-cup of milk. Do the muffins have more milk or more oil?

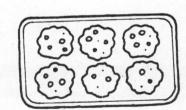

_____

·········· JUST A LITTLE BIT MORE ··········

 Write the mixed number that names the shaded part.

1.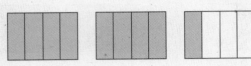

_____

2.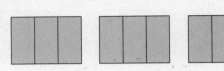

_____

3.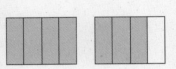

_____

4.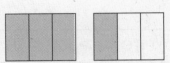

_____

 Use the ruler. Choose the best answer. Circle a, b, or c.

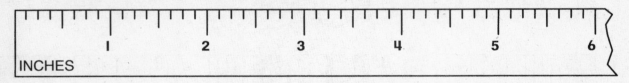

5. Two and one-eighth inches is closest to ____ inches.

a. 1   **b.** 2   **c.** 3

6. One and seven-eighths is closest to ____ inches.

a. 1   **b.** 2   **c.** 3

 Complete the pattern.

7.

$\frac{1}{4}$, $\frac{2}{4}$, $\frac{3}{4}$, 1, $1\frac{1}{4}$, $1\frac{2}{4}$, ____, ____, ____

Real World Connection

Solve.

8. Matt made 4 casseroles. His family ate $2\frac{1}{4}$ of the casseroles for dinner. Shade the casseroles to show what part Matt's family ate.

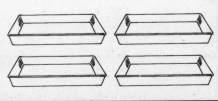

Name _____   Date _____

•••••••••• LESS THAN A WHOLE ••••••••••

Write the decimal for the part that is shaded.

1.

_____

2.

_____

3.

_____

4.

_____

5.

_____

6.

_____

Write each fraction as a decimal.

7. $\frac{2}{10}$ ____   8. $\frac{5}{10}$ ____   9. $\frac{9}{10}$ ____   10. $\frac{3}{10}$ ____

11. $\frac{83}{100}$ ____   12. $\frac{48}{100}$ ____   13. $\frac{9}{100}$ ____   14. $\frac{61}{100}$ ____

Use the place-value chart for Exercises 15–16.

15. In 0.56, what digit is in the hundredths place? _____

16. In 0.34, in what place is the digit 3? _____

Ones	.	Tenths	Hundredths
0	.	5	6
0	.	3	4

Real World Connection

Solve.

17. Marcy has forty-five hundredths cents to buy a drink. How much money does Marcy have?

_____

Fractions and Decimals: Concept Development

Math 3, SV 8047-2

THIRD GRADE MATH
Answer Key

P. 5: 1. 10 **2.** 8 **3.** 12 **4.** 28 **5.** 36 **6.** 9 **7.** 7 **8.** 8 **9.** 48 **10.** 28 **11.** 90 **12.** 600 **13.** 4 r 1 **14.** 800 **15.** 18 **16.** 3 **17.** 1 **18.** 13 **19.** 0 **20.** 20 **21.** 31 **22.** 82 **23.** 87 **24.** 15 r 2 **25.** 310 **26.** 75 **27.** 16 **28.** 318 **29.** 135 **30.** $7.69 **31.** 1689 **32.** 567

P. 6: 1. 7 + 8 = 15 paint brushes **2.** 400 people **3.** $2.05 **4.** 3:30 **5.** 89¢ **6.** 24 crayons **7.** 16 feet **8.** more

P. 7: 1. 8 **2.** 10 **3.** 8 **4.** 9 **5.** 8 **6.** 11 **7.** 11 **8.** 12 **9.** 15 **10.** 14 **11.** 13 **12.** 11 **13.** 12 **14.** 10 **15.** 9 **16.** 11 **17.** 16 **18.** 10 **19.** 15 **20.** 10 **21.** 4 + 2 = 6 frogs

P. 8: 1. 12 **2.** 9 **3.** 6 **4.** 15 **5.** 15 **6.** 13 **7.** 17 **8.** 5 **9.** 10 **10.** 13 **11.** 11 **12.** 4 **13.** 15 **14.** 11 **15.** 13 **16.** 11 **17.** 8 **18.** 17 **19.** 14 **20.** 14 **21.** 16 **22.** 13 **23.** 18 **24.** 16 **25.** 9 **26.** 14 **27.** 10 **28.** 12 **29.** 15 **30.** 8 + 9 = 17 stamps

P. 9: 1. 15 **2.** 15 **3.** 4 **4.** 5 **5.** 5 **6.** 6 **7.** 2 **8.** 8 **9.** 9 **10.** 7 **11.** 12, 12 **12.** 14, 14 **13.** 12, 12 **14.** 7 + 8 = 15 **15.** 4 + 9 = 13 **16.** 7 + 0 = 7 fish

P. 10: 1. 13, yes **2.** 12 **3.** 14 **4.** 12 **5.** 18 **6.** 12 **7.** 11 **8.** 13 **9.** 11 **10.** 15 **11.** 18 **12.** 13 **13.** 17 **14.** 17 **15.** 13 **16.** 13 **17.** 17 **18.** 18 **19.** 15 **20.** 11 **21.** 18 **22.** 15 **23.** 6 + 4 + 3 = 13 dogs

P. 11: 1. 6 **2.** 2 **3.** 4 **4.** 3 **5.** 4 **6.** 4 **7.** 7 **8.** 2 **9.** 3 **10.** 3 **11.** 3 **12.** 5 **13.** 1 **14.** 2 **15.** 2 **16.** 7 **17.** 5 **18.** 2 **19.** 1 **20.** 8 − 5 = 3 grasshoppers

P. 12: 1. 0 **2.** 9 **3.** 0 **4.** 10 **5.** 5 **6.** 6 **7.** 9 **8.** 9 **9.** 0 **10.** 0 **11.** 0 **12.** 5 **13.** 5 **14.** 8 **15.** 0 **16.** 5 **17.** 0 **18.** 7 **19.** 7 − 7 = 0 candles

P. 13: 1. 4, 8, 12 **2.** 6, 7, 13 **3.** 7 + 8 = 15, 8 + 7 = 15, 15 − 8 = 7, 15 − 7 = 8 **4.** 9 + 4 = 13, 4 + 9 = 13, 13 − 9 = 4, 13 − 4 = 9 **5.** 6 + 8 = 14, 8 + 6 = 14, 14 − 6 = 8, 14 − 8 = 6 **6.** 6, 9, 6, 9 **7.** 3 + 4 = 7 people, 4 + 3 = 7, 7 − 4 = 3, 7 − 3 = 4

P. 14: 1. 7 **2.** 9 **3.** 6 **4.** 8 **5.** 9 **6.** 9 **7.** 4 **8.** 5 **9.** 9 **10.** 13 **11.** 14 **12.** 6 **13.** 8 **14.** 0 **15.** 18 **16.** 8 **17.** 8 **18.** 8 **19.** 6 **20.** + **21.** − **22.** − **23.** − **24.** + **25.** + **26.** − **27.** − **28.** − **29.** 7 + 5 = 12 tracks

P. 15: 1. Elaine—8 gerbils, Juanita—6 gerbils **2.** noon—6 minutes, after dinner—9 minutes **3.** fish book—$7, bird magazine—$9 **4.** 11 lionheads, 6 fantails **5.** 7 chickens

P. 16: 1. 285 **2.** 433 **3.** 723 **4.** 109 **5.** 475 **6.** 316 **7.** 579 **8.** 740 **9.** 485 **10.** 610 **11.** 683 **12.** 947

P. 17: 1. < **2.** > **3.** = **4.** < **5.** > **6.** > **7.** < **8.** > **9.** > **10.** = **11.** < **12.** < **13.** > **14.** < **15.** Blue Mound **16.** Clarkville

P. 18: 1. 80, 83, 87 **2.** 31, 35, 38 **3.** 92, 94, 96 **4.** 246, 251, 297 **5.** 803, 830, 897 **6.** 505, 550, 555 **7.** 373, 341, 337 **8.** 698, 689, 675 **9.** 762, 750, 726 **10.** 515, 510, 501 **11.** 432, 430, 423 **12.** 970, 957, 907 **13.** Police Station **14.** Electric Company, City Hall, Fire Station, Police Station

P. 19: 1. 40 **2.** 80 **3.** 90 **4.** 60¢ **5.** 30¢ **6.** 50¢ **7.** 60 **8.** 90 **9.** 50 **10.** 83, 78, 75 **11.** 71¢, 65¢, 67¢, 69¢ **12.** 800 **13.** 700 **14.** 700 **15.** 800 **16.** 600 **17.** 300 **18.** 800 **19.** 900 **20.** 300 **21.** 500 **22.** 200 **23.** 500 **24.** 400 people

P. 20: 1. 2,143 **2.** 1,365 **3.** 8 tens, 7 ones **4.** 4 hundreds, 3 tens, 2 ones **5.** 9 hundreds, 0 tens, 5 ones **6.** 4 thousands, 7 hundreds, 0 tens, 7 ones **7.** 6 thousands, 0 hundreds, 2 tens, 4 ones **8.** 7 thousands, 1 hundred, 4 tens, 5 ones **9.** 2 thousands, 0 hundreds, 0 tens, 1 one **10.** $1,427

P. 21: 1. 38,471 **2.** 46,035 **3.** 54,723 **4.** 30,403 **5.** > **6.** > **7.** > **8.** > **9.** < **10.** = **11.** 2,345; 12,123; 22,486 **12.** 23,676; 32,076; 32,570 **13.** 68,921; 69,129; 70,291 **14.** 99,099; 99,900; 99,909 **15.** balloon, stuffed lion, clown hat, drink

P. 22: 1. 500 **2.** 5,000 **3.** 50,000 **4.** 500,000 **5.** 232,074 **6.** 70,820 **7.** 32,096; 41,096; 131,096 **8.** 250,861; 259,861; 349,861 **9.** 891,421; 900,421; 990,421 **10.** 622,940; 631,940; 721,940 **11.** 169,300 miles

P. 23: 1. even **2.** odd **3.** odd **4.** even **5.** odd **6.** even **7.** 20, 50, 60 **8.** 25, 15, 10 **9.** 29, 31, 35 **10.** 28, 35, 42 **11.** 28, 36, 44 **12.** 36, 30, 24 **13.** 21, 25, 29, 33, 37, 41, 45, 49

P. 24: 1. Vicki **2.** east **3.** 21, 22, 23, or 24 pounds **4.** 31,700; 23,000; 22,300; 9,910; 7,550; Students circle Superior, 31,700 and Huron, 23,000. **5.** 275,000 people

P. 25: 1. 50 + 20 = 70 **2.** 20 + 70 = 90 **3.** 90 − 40 = 50 **4.** 90 + 50 = 140 **5.** 70 − 30 = 40 **6.** 60 + 100 = 160 **7.** 40 + 70 = 110 **8.** 60 − 20 = 40 **9.** 70 + 20 = 90 **10.** plane and ball

P. 26: 1. 105 **2.** 151 **3.** 106 **4.** 122 **5.** 114 **6.** 125 **7.** 134 **8.** 78 **9.** 120 **10.** 78 **11.** 145 **12.** 58 **13.** 126 **14.** 138 **15.** 152 **16.** 106 **17.** 141 **18.** 135 **19.** 13 + 16 + 11 = 40 miles

P. 27: 1. 69 **2.** 33 **3.** 41 **4.** 44 **5.** 16 **6.** 21 **7.** 18 **8.** 37 **9.** 44 **10.** 23 **11.** 52 **12.** 10 **13.** 60 **14.** 9 **15.** 28 **16.** 5 **17.** 25 − 19 = 6 floors

P. 28: 1. 800 **2.** 1,100 **3.** 400 **4.** 1,000 **5.** 1,100 **6.** 700 **7.** 1,700 **8.** 1,500 **9.** 900 **10.** 1,300 **11.** 600 **12.** 800 **13.** 700 **14.** 900 **15.** 800 **16.** 800 **17.** 278 + 112 = about 400 tires

P. 29: 1. 677 **2.** 1,378 **3.** 724 **4.** 162 **5.** 1,179 **6.** 894 **7.** 893 **8.** 1,099 **9.** 277 **10.** 847 **11.** 492 **12.** 939 **13.** 963 **14.** 1,127 **15.** 893 **16.** 865 **17.** 284 + 121 = 405 problems

P. 30: 1. $6.89 **2.** $8.13 **3.** $11.04 **4.** $9.87 **5.** $10.43 **6.** $13.20 **7.** $12.29 **8.** $16.28 **9.** $17.80 **10.** $13.72 **11.** $14.59 **12.** $12.37 **13.** $7.81 **14.** $9.68 **15.** $5.24 **16.** $8.93 **17.** $2.20 + $2.20 = $4.40

P. 31: 1. 217 **2.** 426 **3.** 544 **4.** 603 **5.** 327 **6.** 718 **7.** 602 **8.** 925 **9.** 537 **10.** 250 **11.** 355 **12.** 225 **13.** 528 **14.** 503 **15.** 604 **16.** 612 − 480 = 132 tickets

P. 32: 1. 87 **2.** 581 **3.** 377 **4.** 537 **5.** 114 **6.** 190 **7.** 135 **8.** 265 **9.** 20 **10.** 344 **11.** 125 **12.** 151 **13.** 97 **14.** 288 **15.** 286 **16.** 214 − 181 = 33 points

P. 33: 1. 245, b **2.** 451, b **3.** 104, c **4.** 574,a **5.** 524 **6.** 512 **7.** 154 **8.** 108 **9.** 535 **10.** 200 − 115 = 85 times

P. 34: 1. 47 **2.** 81 **3.** 75 **4.** 90 **5.** 23 **6.** 35 **7.** 612 **8.** 118 **9.** 789 **10.** 125 **11.** 1,689 **12.** 154 **13.** 308 **14.** 535 **15.** 990 **16.** 199 **17.** 593 **18.** 362 **19.** 1 **20.** 1,371 **21.** $4.11 **22.** 300 − 146 = 154 yards

P. 35: 1. 9 people **2.** 800 people **3.** $38 **4.** 104 more kilometers per hour **5.** 311 more kilometers

P. 36: 1. Sunday **2.** Thursday **3.** July 20 **4.** July 5 **5.** 31 days **6.** 5 Fridays **7.** July 14 **8.** Sunday **9.** 9 days

P. 37: 1. movie **2.** read **3.** make a bed **4.** 3 hours **5.** 40 minutes **6.** jump rope

P. 38: 1. 11:00 **2.** 3:00 **3.** 7:00 **4.** 10 **5.** 45 **6.** 30 **7.** 10:15, 1:45, 4:30 **8.** 11:15, 2:45, 5:30 **9.** 10:45, 2:15, 5:00 **10.** 3:00

P. 39: 1. 10, 15, 20, 25, 30 **2.** 10, 15 **3.** 10, 15, 20, 25, 30 **4.** 10, 15, 20 **5.** 4:34 **6.** 7:39 **7.** 3:24 **8.** 3:15

P. 40: 1. Saturday **2.** Students draw clock hands to show 4:40, 4:40 **3.** 3:30 **4.** 2 hours **5.** 2:15

P. 41: 1. 48¢ **2.** 80¢ **3.** 48¢ **4.** $2.38 **5.** $6.12 **6.** $3.95 **7.** $1.17 **8.** $2.46 **9.** $5.52 **10.** bear, ball

P. 42: 1. a **2.** c **3.** Answers will vary. **4.** Answers will vary. **5.** yes

P. 43: 1. Answers will vary. **2.** Answers will vary. **3.** Answers will vary. **4.** 2 pennies, 1 nickel, 1 dime, 1 quarter **5.** 2 pennies, 1 quarter **6.** $2.21

P. 44: 1. 2 quarters, 2 pennies **2.** no **3.** 2 pennies **4.** Answers will vary. **5.** 10 dimes

P. 45: 1. 6, 6, 6 **2.** 14, 14, 14 **3.** 6, 6 **4.** 8 + 8 = 16, 8 × 2 = 16 **5.** 6 + 6 + 6 = 18, 3 × 6 = 18 **6.** Students show 4 groups of 4. **7.** Students show 3 groups of 3. **8.** 3 + 3 + 3 + 3 = 12 stickers, 4 × 3 = 12 stickers

P. 46: 1. 10 **2.** 12 **3.** 16 **4.** 4 × 2 = 8 **5.** 2 × 7 = 14 **6.** 2 × 3 = 6 **7.** 10 **8.** 18 **9.** 8 **10.** 14 **11.** 16 **12.** 12 **13.** 4 **14.** 6 **15.** 6 × 2 = 12 roses

P. 47: 1. 24 **2.** 12 **3.** 18 **4.** 4 × 3 = 12 **5.** 3 × 7 = 21 **6.** 3 × 9 = 27 **7.** 6 **8.** 27 **9.** 24 **10.** 21 **11.** 15 **12.** 18 **13.** 9 **14.** 12 **15.** 5 × 3 = 15 footballs

P. 48: 1. Students show 8 groups of 4. **2.** Students show 4 groups of 4. **3.** Students show 7 groups of 4. **4.** Students show 4 groups of 5. **5.** Students show 5 groups of 3. **6.** Students show 6 groups of 5. **7.** 40 **8.** 24 **9.** 35 **10.** 25 **11.** 36 **12.** 45 **13.** 12 **14.** 10 **15.** 12 **16.** 24 **17.** 16 **18.** 20 **19.** 40 **20.** 30 **21.** 28 **22.** 45 **23.** 6 × 4 = 24 animals

P. 49: 1. 0 **2.** 8 **3.** 7 **4.** 0 **5.** 0 **6.** 3 **7.** 9 **8.** 0 **9.** 0 **10.** 10 **11.** 0 **12.** 6 **13.** 0 **14.** 3 **15.** 0 **16.** 0 **17.** 1 **18.** 5 **19.** 0 **20.** 4 **21.** 0 **22.** 0 **23.** 2 **24.** 0 **25.** 8 **26.** 0 **27.** 6 **28.** 8 × 0 = 0 stamps

P. 50: 1. 3 × 3 = 9 **2.** 2 × 5 = 10 **3.** 4 × 5 = 20 **4.** 2 × 8 = 16 **5.** 3 × 6 = 18 **6.** 4 × 4 = 16 **7.** 12 **8.** 21 **9.** 10 **10.** 14 **11.** 24 **12.** 32 **13.** 25 **14.** 9 **15.** 12 **16.** 16 **17.** 12 **18.** 27 **19.** 20 **20.** 15 **21.** 30 **22.** 10 **23.** 12 **24.** 45 **25.** 5 × 4 = 20 crayons

P. 51: 1. 54 **2.** 56 **3.** 30 **4.** 42 **5.** 49 **6.** 48 **7.** 18 **8.** 24 **9.** 36 **10.** 48 **11.** 30 **12.** 21 **13.** 63 **14.** 35 **15.** 42 **16.** 14 **17.** 6 × 8 = 48 students

P. 52: 1. 0, 8, 16, 24, 32, 40, 48, 56, 64, 72 **2.** 0, 9, 18, 27, 36, 45, 54, 63, 72, 81 **3.** 27 **4.** 32 **5.** 8 **6.** 18 **7.** 56 **8.** 81 **9.** 40 **10.** 72 **11.** 24 **12.** 63 **13.** 36 **14.** 54 **15.** 0 **16.** 28 **17.** 36 **18.** 48 **19.** 36 **20.** 18 **21.** 9 **22.** 64 **23.** 63 **24.** 16 **25.** 45 **26.** 7 × 9 = 63 years

P. 53: 1. 15 **2.** 35 **3.** 72 **4.** 14 **5.** 8 **6.** 36 **7.** 24 **8.** 42 **9.** 16 **10.** 54 **11.** 40 **12.** 7 **13.** 45 **14.** 0 **15.** 35 **16.** 72 **17.** 36 **18.** 21 **19.** 25 **20.** 32 **21.** 4 **22.** 0 **23.** 9 **24.** 8 **25.** 0 **26.** 7 **27.** 6 **28.** 9 **29.** 10 **30.** 64 **31.** 0 **32.** 24 **33.** 8 × $3 = $24

P. 54: 1. 12 squares **2.** 45¢ **3.** Students draw 4 rows of 4 squares. **4.** 56 buttons **5.** 24 needles

P. 55: 1. 6, 2, 3, 3 **2.** 21, 3, 7, 7 **3.** 12, 3, 4, 4 **4.** 2 **5.** 3 **6.** 4 **7.** 2 cookies

P. 56: 1. 21, 3 **2.** 20, 5 **3.** 3, 2, 6 **4.** 5, 7, 35 **5.** 4 × 6 = 24, 6 × 4 = 24, 24 ÷ 4 = 6, 24 ÷ 6 = 4 **6.** 2 × 5 = 10, 5 × 2 = 10, 10 ÷ 2 = 5, 10 ÷ 5 = 2 **7.** 3 × 9 = 27, 9 × 3 = 27, 27 ÷ 3 = 9, 27 ÷ 9 = 3 **8.** Students draw 6 groups of 3.

P. 57: 1. 6 **2.** 5 **3.** 4 **4.** 7 **5.** 4 **6.** 2 **7.** 6 **8.** 8 **9.** 9 **10.** 5 **11.** 3 **12.** 7 **13.** 8 ÷ 2 = 4 boats

P. 58: 1. 12 ÷ 3 = 4 or 12 ÷ 4 = 3 **2.** 18 ÷ 3 = 6 or 18 ÷ 6 = 3 **3.** 4 **4.** 6 **5.** 7 **6.** 4 **7.** 9 **8.** 8 **9.** 3 **10.** 2 **11.** 2 **12.** 6 **13.** 7 **14.** 9 **15.** 6 **16.** 1 **17.** 3 **18.** 5 **19.** 8 **20.** 4 **21.** ÷ **22.** × **23.** ÷ **24.** × **25.** ÷ **26.** ÷ **27.** × **28.** × **29.** 15 ÷ 3 = 5 chips

P. 59: 1. 12 ÷ 4 = 3 or 12 ÷ 3 = 4 **2.** 30 ÷ 5 = 6 or 30 ÷ 6 = 5 **3.** 6 **4.** 9 **5.** 2 **6.** 4 **7.** 7 **8.** 3 **9.** 5 **10.** 6 **11.** 4 **12.** 6 **13.** 8 **14.** 9 **15.** 3 **16.** 3 **17.** 7 **18.** 4 **19.** 6 **20.** 5 **21.** 5 **22.** 7 **23.** 9 **24.** 8 **25.** 2 **26.** 8 **27.** 6 **28.** 2 **29.** 4 **30.** 35 ÷ 5 = 7 colors

P. 60: 1. 1 **2.** 0 **3.** 7 **4.** 1 **5.** 8 **6.** 0 **7.** 1 **8.** 0 **9.** 0 **10.** 0 **11.** 5 **12.** 1 **13.** 6 **14.** 1 **15.** 3 **16.** 0 **17.** 1 **18.** 0 **19.** 4 **20.** 1 **21.** 0 **22.** 1 **23.** 0 **24.** 9 **25.** 8 ÷ 8 = 1 ball

P. 61: 1. 4, Students draw 4 groups of 4. **2.** 2, Students draw 5 groups of 2. **3.** 1, Students draw 3 groups of 1. **4.** 15 ÷ 3 = 5, 15 ÷ 5 = 3 **5.** 12 ÷ 2 = 6, 12 ÷ 6 = 2 **6.** 4 ÷ 1 = 4, 4 ÷ 4 = 1 **7.** 6 **8.** 6 **9.** 5 **10.** 0 **11.** 3 **12.** 7 **13.** 3 **14.** 5 **15.** 7 **16.** 4 **17.** 8 **18.** 8 **19.** 8 **20.** 4 **21.** 1 **22.** 3 **23.** 9 **24.** 4 **25.** 24 ÷ 3 = 8 teams

www.svschoolsupply.com

© Steck-Vaughn Company

95

Math 3, SV 8047-2

P. 62: 1. 3 **2.** 4 **3.** 0 **4.** 2 **5.** 9 **6.** 6 **7.** 3 **8.** 7 **9.** 8
10. 0 **11.** 6 **12.** 8 **13.** 4 **14.** 1 **15.** 5 **16.** 2 **17.** 9
18. 7 **19.** 1 **20.** 5 **21.** 6 **22.** 8 **23.** 7 **24.** 6 **25.** 5
26. 7 **27.** 8 **28.** 24 ÷ 6 = 4 kittens

P. 63: 1. 6 **2.** 8 **3.** 9 **4.** 7 **5.** 2 **6.** 9 **7.** 6 **8.** 4 **9.** 5
10. 6 **11.** 9 **12.** 9 **13.** 1 **14.** 8 **15.** 5 **16.** 0 **17.** 7
18. 4 **19.** 3 **20.** 8 **21.** 5 **22.** 8 **23.** 1 **24.** 6 **25.** 9
26. 9 **27.** 6 **28.** 81 ÷ 9 = 9 flowers

P. 64: 1. 9 **2.** 9 **3.** 7 **4.** 1 **5.** 5 **6.** 9 **7.** 4 **8.** 3 **9.** 0
10. 7 **11.** 5 **12.** 4 **13.** 9 **14.** 0 **15.** 9 **16.** 6 **17.** 6
18. 1 **19.** 9 **20.** 8 **21.** 7 **22.** 56 ÷ 8 = 7 children

P. 65: 1. 2, 1 **2.** 2, 2 **3.** 9 r 1 **4.** 8 **5.** 5 r 2 **6.** 4 r 3
7. 8 r 1 **8.** 9 r 2 **9.** 5 r 7 **10.** 6 r 1 **11.** 7 **12.** 9 r 3
13. 5 r 2 **14.** 4 r 3 **15.** 6 r 6 **16.** 8 r 2 **17.** 9 **18.** 3 r 4
19. 25 ÷ 4 = 6 r 1, 1 muffin

P. 66: Check to see students correctly check work
using multiplication and adding in the remainders.
1. 21 r 2 **2.** 15 r 2 **3.** 17 r 1 **4.** 13 r 1 **5.** 27 r 1
6. 19 r 1 **7.** 13 r 4 **8.** 54 ÷ 4 = 13 r 2 stamps

P. 67: 1. 3 × 4 = 12, 4 × 3 = 12, 12 ÷ 3 = 4, 12 ÷ 4 = 3
2. 2 × 6 = 12, 6 × 2 = 12, 12 ÷ 2 = 6, 12 ÷ 6 = 2 **3.** 18
4. 2 **5.** 9 **6.** 40 **7.** 7 **8.** 9 **9.** 45 **10.** 0 **11.** 9 **12.** 4
13. 7 **14.** 56 **15.** 4 **16.** 36 **17.** 4 r 2 **18.** 72
19. 14 r 2 **20.** 24 **21.** 46 ÷ 4 = 11 r 2 cars or 11 cars

P. 68: 1. 9 duets **2.** 4 pieces **3.** 4 students
4. 16 minutes **5.** $3

P. 69: 1. 3 × 3 = 9 **2.** 3 × 30 = 90 **3.** 3 × 300 = 900
4. ones, 21; tens, 21, 210; hundreds, 21, 2,100
5. 12, 120, 1,200 **6.** 27, 270, 2,700 **7.** 30, 300, 3,000
8. 200 **9.** 3,600 **10.** 150 **11.** 560 **12.** 5,400
13. 60 × 8 = 480 windows

P. 70: 1. 60, 60, 60 **2.** 72, 72, 72 **3.** 39 **4.** 75 **5.** 56
6. 96 **7.** 64 **8.** 86 **9.** 31 × 2 = 62 stamps

P. 71: 1. 54 **2.** 54 **3.** 84 **4.** 76 **5.** 85 **6.** 76 **7.** 92
8. 68 **9.** 80 **10.** 88 **11.** 75 **12.** 36 **13.** 126 **14.** 126
15. 166 **16.** 144 **17.** 355 **18.** 96 **19.** 170 **20.** 186
21. 132 **22.** 168 **23.** 19 × 2 = 38 hours

P. 72: 1. 824 **2.** 645 **3.** 987 **4.** 548 **5.** 900 **6.** 750
7. 1,710 **8.** 936 **9.** 2,364 **10.** 3,296 **11.** 924
12. 1,080 **13.** 4,515 **14.** 892 **15.** 1,298 **16.** 820
17. 870 **18.** 168 **19.** 560 **20.** 424 **21.** 513 **22.** 744
23. 112 × 7 = 784 acres

P. 73: 1. $280 **2.** 1,000 pounds **3.** 21 bags
4. 23 bags **5.** 1,528 more cans

P. 74: 1. cylinder **2.** sphere **3.** rectangular prism
4. pyramid **5.** cube **6.** cone **7.** rectangular prism
8. pyramid **9.** cylinder **10.** Answers will vary.

P. 75: 1. circle **2.** rectangle **3.** triangle **4.** pentagon
5. circle **6.** square **7.** square **8.** rectangle **9.** triangle
10. circle **11.** pentagon **12.** octagon

P. 76: 1. yes **2.** no **3.** yes **4.** yes **5.** second shape
6. third shape **7.** third shape **8.** Students draw the
same sized shape.

P. 77: 1. yes **2.** yes **3.** no **4.** yes **5.** yes **6.** yes
7. no **8.** yes **9.** yes **10.** no **11.** Answers will vary.

P. 78: 1.–7. Answers will vary. **8.** 16 × 4 = 64 steps

P. 79: 1. 8 sq. units **2.** 12 sq. units **3.** 6 sq. units
4. 16 sq. units **5.** 15 sq. units **6.** 18 sq. units
7.–9. Answers will vary. **10.** Students shade 12 sq. units.

P. 80: 1. 8 cubes **2.** 12 cubes **3.** 11 cubes
4. 10 cubes **5.** 24 cubes **6.** 18 cubes **7.** 11 cubes
8. 3 cubes **9.** 19 cubes **10.** 24 × 2 = 48 cubes

P. 81: 1. 18 cubes **2.** 140 steps **3.** 35 sq. units
4. sphere and cylinder **5.** Students draw a line
from the valley between the humps of the heart to
the point.

P. 82: 1. 1 in. **2.** 3 in. **3.** 6 in. **4.–6.** Measure lines.
7. 11 inches **8.** 2 miles **9.** 2 feet **10.** 20 miles
11. 2 × 5 = 10 in.

P. 83: 1. ounce **2.** pound **3.** ounce **4.** pound **5.** c
6. gal **7.** gal **8.** pt **9.** 1 pound **10.** 8 ounces
11. 1 quart **12.** 1 gallon **13.** 5 gallons **14.** 1 cup
15. less than

P. 84: 1. 120°F **2.** 30°F **3.** 85°F **4.** 68°F **5.** 46°F
6. 80°F **7.** 22°F **8.** 62°F

P. 85: 1. 8 cm **2.** 5 cm **3.–5.** Measure lines.
6. 8 meters **7.** 1 meter **8.** 700 kilometers
9. 30 meters **10.** 9 × 7 = 63 minutes

P. 86: 1. gram **2.** gram **3.** kilogram **4.** milliliter
5. milliliter **6.** liter **7.** 2 L **8.** 250 mL **9.** 6 L
10. 10 kg **11.** 65 g **12.** 25 kg **13.** 500 − 175 = 325 mL

P. 87: 1. 70°C **2.** 0°C **3.** 20°C **4.** 20°C **5.** 30°C
6. −5°C **7.** 12°C **8.** 26°C **9.** −10°C
10. 150°C − 20°C = 130°C

P. 88: 1. 36 in. **2.** 16 meters **3.** 24 pounds
4. 84°F **5.** 5 L

P. 89: 1. 4/5 **2.** 2/4 **3.** 1/3 **4.** 3/4 **5.** 5/8 **6.** 2/6
7. 4/5 **8.** 4/4 **9.** 1/3 **10.** 2/5 **11.** 4/6
12. Students shade 1 part.

P. 90: 1. true **2.** false **3.** true **4.** false **5.** true
6. false **7.** 4 **8.** 1 **9.** 4 **10.** 2 **11.** 1 **12.** 3
13. 2, Students shade 2 parts.

P. 91: 1. < **2.** > **3.** > **4.** < **5.** = **6.** > **7.** = **8.** >
9. < **10.** more milk

P. 92: 1. 2 1/4 **2.** 2 2/3 **3.** 1 3/4 **4.** 1 1/3 **5.** b **6.** b
7. 1 3/4, 2, 2 1/4 **8.** Students shade 2 whole
casseroles and 1/4 of another.

P. 93: 1. 0.7 **2.** 0.1 **3.** 0.4 **4.** 0.20 **5.** 0.37 **6.** 0.62
7. 0.2 **8.** 0.5 **9.** 0.9 **10.** 0.3 **11.** 0.83 **12.** 0.48
13. 0.09 **14.** 0.61 **15.** 6 **16.** tenths **17.** 45¢ or $0.45

Math 3, SV 8047-2